the world of automobiles

An Illustrated Encyclopedia of the Motor Car

COLUMBIA HOUSE/New York

Consultant Editor: Tom Northey
Executive Editor: Ian Ward
Editorial Director: Brian Innes
Assistant Editors: Laurie Caddell
Mike Winfield
Art Editor: David Goodman
Art Assistant: John Heritage
Picture Research: Evan Davies
Mirco Decet
Cover Design: Harry W. Fass
Production Manager: Warren Bright

contributors
ANDY ANDERSON:
Oval-Circuit Racing
Petty
DAVID BURGESS WISE:
Oldsmobile
Otto
Owen Magnetic
Paris Racing
Pennington
Petre
LAURIE CADDELL: Peterson
MIKE KETTLEWELL: Oldfield
Ontario
Osca
Palliser
Parkes
Parnell
Penske
Pescarolo
KARL LUDVIGSEN: Packard
FREDERICK PALE: Overtaking
L. J. K. SETRIGHT: OM
Opel
Overdrive
Panhard

Pegaso
Petroleum
IAN WARD: Panther
MIKE WINFIELD: Pace
Peerless
WORDSMITHS LTD:
Oil Filter
Oil Pump
Paintwork Repairs
Panel Beating

Contents

		Page
BETTER DRIVING	Overtaking: Passing in Safety	1608
CARS OF TODAY	Oldsmobile Omega	1575
	Oldsmobile Toronado	1576
	Opel Manta	1592
	Opel Commodore GS/E Coupe	1592
	Panther J72	1643
THE GREAT CARS	Oldsmobile: A Horse Without the Smell	1566
	OM: Never What It Seemed	1577
	Opel: Simple Engineering and Commercial Courage	1583
	OSCA: A Maserati Without the Name	1594
	Owen: A British Motoring Enigma	1609
	Owen Magnetic: "Car of 1000 Speeds"	1611
	Packard: Fine Engineering, Long Life and Luxury	1614
	Panhard: The Recusant Pioneers	1629
	Panther: The New Breed of Cat	1638
	Peerless: A Victim of Circumstance	1654
	Pegaso: The Ricart Diamond and the Flying Horse	1658
	Pennington: A Mechanical Charlatan	1661
HOW IT WORKS	Oil Filter: Taking the Dirt Out of the Oil	1561
	Oil Pump: Keeping the Lubricant on the Move	1563
	Otto Cycle: First With the Four Stroke	1599
	Overdrive: The Cruising Gear	1605
	Paintwork Repairs: The Finishing Touch	1621
	Panel Beating: Knocking It Into Shape	1626
	Petroleum: Black Gold	1673
WHO'S WHO	Oldfield: A Cigar Chewing Entertainer	1565
	Pace: Motor Racing's Pace-Setter	1613
	Parkes: A Man for All Occasions	1644
	Parnell: Pressing On for Britain	1651
	Penske: The Name of the Game Is Winning	1665
	Pescarolo: Sports-Car Superstar	1669
	Peterson: Superswede	1670
	Petre: A Touch of Class	1672
	Petty: Motor Racing's Most Successful Family?	1679
WORLD OF SPEED	Ontario: An Illusion of Grandeur	1581
	Palliser: The Jet Pilot's Racing Cars	1624
	Paris Races: The Races That Started It All	1646
WORLD OF SPORT	Oval-Circuit Racing: Speed in the Stadium	1601

TAKING THE DIRT OUT OF THE OIL

No matter how efficient the lubricant, particles find their way into it and must be filtered out

IN MOST ENGINES, the oil drawn into the oil pump from the sump has to pass through a comparatively coarse gauze strainer; this prevents the large particles and sludge that sink to the bottom of the sump from entering the pump.

There are, however, many finer particles and undesirable pollutants that find their way into lubricating oil: most of these are varnishes, gums, resins and acids,

Below; two types of filtration system, full flow (*left*) and the earlier and less efficient partial flow

Bottom; a selection of filters made by AP

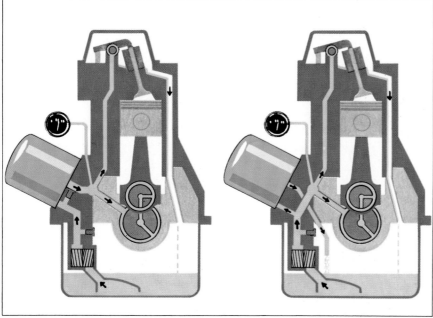

formed partly by oil decomposition and partly by condensed crankcase vapours; next come carbon, a by-product of combustion, and water from condensation formed in the crankcase when the engine is cold (carbon and water combine to form sludge). Apart from this, particles of metal wear off all rubbing surfaces, especially when the engine is new; silica, or road-dust particles, may enter through the air filter or crankcase breather; finally, there are lead and iron oxides.

The modern oil filter removes a very large percentage of all these contaminants. Up to World War II, many engines were protected by the sump strainer only; then came the partial-flow filter, which cleaned about ten per cent of the total oil flow and effectively filtered the whole of the oil about ten times per hour. For some years, however, most manufacturers have fitted full-flow filters, which are situated close to the outlet side of the oil pump. A by-pass valve, set to open at between 10 and 15 lb per sq in is often provided in case the filter becomes blocked.

Early filters consisted of a roll of felt or flannel, but these were almost too efficient and tended to clog up prematurely, obstructing the oil flow. Wool, cotton

waste, mineral wool, sisal grass and resin-impregnated fibre blocks have all been used as filters. Although some of these materials are still in use, the trend is to use a strong, resin-impregnated paper, pleated to offer a large surface area and therefore less resistance to the oil flow. One typical modern filter offers 1000 sq in of filter area and retains particles down to 5 micrometres (five-millionths of a metre) in size. Support is given by a perforated metal container and strict attention is paid, during manufacture, to sealing the ends of the pleats. There is also a 'dual media' filter available, with a full-flow section of relatively coarse material and a lower velocity cleaning section for maximum retention of particles.

There are two main forms of filter, the renewable cartridge and the throw-away canister, and there are many variations of both types.

The simplest type is the self-supporting screw-in canister, which often protrudes horizontally from the side of the crankcase. Other types are fitted beneath a bracket housing the oilway connections, oil-pressure relief valve and oil-pressure connection to a gauge or warning light. The filter is housed in a metal container secured, usually, by a long bolt from below. The container may hold a renewable cartridge or is often of the throw-away type.

The centrifugal filter (more strictly, an oil *cleaner*) has an entirely different construction and method of operation. It is normally located behind the crankshaft pulley and relies for its effectiveness on particles being thrown outwards by small vanes to lodge among the sludge in the outer cavities of the cover. A strainer is included in the assembly.

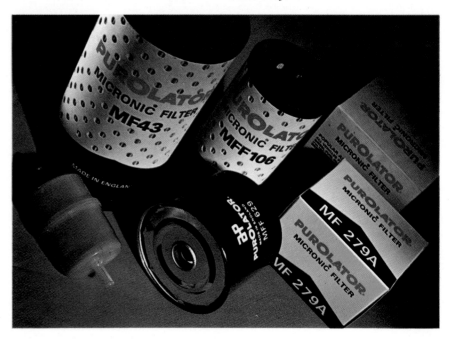

Seals and gaskets

In general, undamaged cork gaskets and similar flat items may be used again. When a rubber seal is used with a filter canister, a new seal is provided with the new filter. If this seal is of square section, make sure that it lies flat; also ensure that the old seal is removed —it sometimes lies in a narrow channel and has to be prised out carefully. Lightly grease both sides of seals or gaskets before refitting them. Examine any interior seals (not normally requiring replacement) to ensure that they have not deteriorated.

Replacing cartridge filter

Unscrew the centre bolt and ease off the filter, taking care not to damage the gasket. Note the arrangement of any washers, spacers or springs that will be required on replacement. Discard the cartridge and wash out the container and fittings with petrol. Allow the parts to dry, before replacing them together with the new cartridge.

Replacing throw-away filters

The vertical filter is unscrewed either by a central bolt or by a hexagon shape on the bottom of the canister. The smaller, horizontal type incorporates a screw fixing; it can usually be unscrewed with two hands, by use of a strap wrench or by piercing it with a screwdriver to gain extra leverage.

The centrifugal filter must be dismantled for cleaning. This normally entails removal of the drive belt, crankshaft pulley and filter cover. The strainer and other components should be carefully washed in petrol, dried and replaced.

Testing

After replacing the filter unit, strainer and drain plug, fill the sump with the correct quantity of oil, then start the engine and watch the oil-pressure gauge or warning light. Pressure may take a little longer than usual to build up while the oil fills the voids in the new filter and the drained system. After a few minutes' run, examine the filter carefully for any signs of leaking oil; if necessary, reseat the filter after checking the seals, re-tighten and check again.

Renewal period

Oil filters are normally renewed every 6000 or 9000 miles, or according to the manufacturer's instructions. Remember that however efficiently the filter removes dirt particles and other pollutants, it is not everlasting. A few pints of oil and a new filter are always cheaper than a damaged engine.   GH

Right: two paper-type oil filters, one complete and the other with a section of the folded element cut away to reveal the perforated metal tube which runs down the centre of the filter; the paper is usually impregnated with resin and is capable of retaining particles as small as 5 micrometres

KEEPING THE LUBRICANT ON THE MOVE

Oil must be kept circulating in order to maintain low temperature and adequate lubrication

MANY HIGHLY STRESSED, rapidly moving components in a modern internal-combustion engine need constant lubrication if seizure or excessive wear are to be avoided. The function of an oil pump is to supply oil, under pressure, to those parts of the engine which require this positive lubrication.

The most common form of oil pump used to be the gear type. It consists of two meshing gears, which rotate inside a close-fitted housing. As the gears rotate they carry oil around, against the housing. The meshing of the gear teeth forces the oil out, into the pump discharge tube.

This gear-type oil pump produces a positive flow of oil to the various parts of the engine to which it is directed. If the flow is blocked, the oil pressure can increase sufficiently to damage the pump. Alternatively, if the engine oil is particularly thick, the pressure required to force the cold oil through the small bearing clearances can cause a similar pressure build-up, damaging the pump. To eliminate these possibilities an oil-pressure relief valve is fitted. This returns oil to the sump, or to the oil tank if a dry-sump system is used, when the pressure created exceeds a predetermined value.

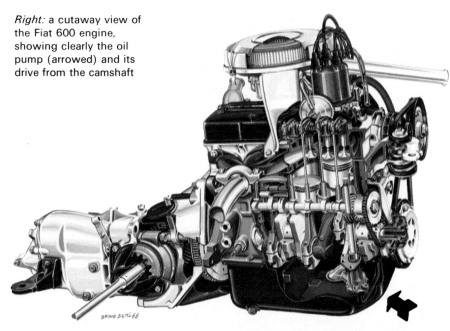

Right: a cutaway view of the Fiat 600 engine, showing clearly the oil pump (arrowed) and its drive from the camshaft

Another form of oil pump, more common than the gear type, is the rotor variety. This consists of a rotor, with four or five external lobes, which rotates inside an outer ring (termed a stator) having five or six internal lobes. The axis of the inner rotor is offset from the axis of the outer ring. The effect is that, although the outer ring is driven by the inner rotor, the volume between the lobes varies as the two rotate. Oil is thus caught between the lobes and forced out into the pump discharge tube.

The action of this type of oil pump can be likened in some ways to the operation of the Wankel or rotary

Above: a partially dismantled vane-type pump, in which the rotor, which has sliding vanes, spins inside an ovalised chamber; the pressure relief valve is seen with its spring

Left: a similar view of a rotor-type pump

engine. The rotor-type oil pump also requires a pressure relief valve. A less common type of oil pump is the rotary-plunger type of pump. This has only one moving part: a worm gear rotates a rotary plunger. A peg engages a profiled groove in the rotary plunger to provide the reciprocating movement, so producing the pumping action. A non-return valve is also necessary. The oil flow from this type of pump is intermittent and the pressure produced is generally lower than that produced by the gear or rotor-type oil pumps. It is therefore inherently unsuitable for many engines, but is used in some engines which utilise roller or ball-races as big-end or main bearings, and as such require only minimal lubrication.

In rare instances a plunger oil pump is reciprocated by an eccentric peg on the end of a shaft, which engages a slot in the plunger. A particular disadvantage of both the gear and rotor-type oil pumps is that after the engine has been stopped, oil can drain back through the system to the sump. Neither of these is therefore entirely suitable for a dry-sump lubrication system which might as an alternative employ a form of plunger pump.

The final type of pump is known as the sliding-vane oil pump. This consists of a four-vaned rotor, the vanes of which form a seal against the walls of an ovalised chamber by being free to slide in and out of the rotor to take up the ovality. As with the rotor-type pump, the volume between the vanes varies as the rotor spins; oil is drawn in as the volume increases and is squeezed out as it decreases. This type tends to wear more quickly than the others.

Most modern internal-combustion engines use a wet-sump lubrication system and the engine bearings are usually of the plain white-metal type. These bearings require only a comparatively low-pressure oil supply, of the order of a few pounds per square inch, to provide adequate lubrication. Oil supplied to a

bearing at one point is drawn around between the two bearing surfaces by rotation. In this way a wedge of oil is formed which is of sufficient strength to take the full load of the bearings.

The high oil pressure produced by a gear, rotor, or vane pump is used to provide a sufficiently fast flow of oil to absorb and carry away heat from the bearing surfaces and other parts of the engine such as the pistons, which would otherwise overheat.

Those engines which use a dry-sump system normally have dual oil pumps. One of these is used to provide oil pressure for lubrication. The second (the 'scavenge' pump) is used to remove the oil from the sump to the oil tank. To prevent a surplus of oil accumulating in the sump, the second pump usually has a larger capacity than the lubricating pump.

Oil pumps require no routine maintenance, although if they incorporate a strainer this should be cleaned periodically. The job need only be done infrequently, when the sump is removed, and only when removing sludge from the sump.

Oil pumps are usually driven from the camshaft or crankshaft through suitable gearing. It is this gearing which is likely to be damaged if the oil-pump outlet has been blocked and the pump has suffered from over-pressure.

It might be thought that constantly being immersed in oil, oil pumps would have an almost indefinite working life. In fact they have a long working life, but they do eventually wear. As a result the oil pump output will in time become insufficient for the requirements of the engine.

Most service manuals specify maximum limits for wear between the components of the oil pump. If these wear limits are exceeded, it is normal practice to change the oil pump as an assembly. Such renewal is generally only undertaken as part of a major engine overhaul or reconditioning.   GH

Above left: a rotor-type of oil pump, with the casing cut away to reveal the two multi-lobed rotors, which squeeze the oil through the pump

Above: a complete screw-in oil pump made by Burman of Birmingham

A cigar chewing entertainer

BERNA ELI 'BARNEY' OLDFIELD was a showman, a rich showman. He specialised in short match races, chiefly on dirt-tracks, shortly after the turn of the century, but he was also an accomplished road racer. Perhaps because of his showmanship on the dirt-tracks, his circuit achievements did not receive the recognition due. In the 1914 Indianapolis 500, for instance, he fought valiantly against tough French opposition in his Stutz and finished fifth, the only American driver of an American car in the first eight.

From a poor family in Wauseon, Ohio, Barney Oldfield was born on 3 June 1878, and left school when he was twelve. He later joked that his first 'driving' job was as a lift boy in a hotel. Bicycle racing became his profession and he won countless events, but in 1902 he had a major break. A fellow cycle-racing friend, Tom Cooper, lent him a petrol-engined vehicle, a tandem racing bike, to race in Salt Lake City, Oldfield's new home town. Several months later, Oldfield heard from Cooper. He and a chap called Henry Ford were building two racing cars—and would Barney like to drive one? He did, and quickly moved east where the cars were under construction.

Oldfield became famous for his driving of the Ford-built *999* and later the *Winton Bullet*, the *Peerless Dragon* and the front-wheel-drive *Christie*. On Memorial Day 1903, he became the first American to cover a mile in a minute during a match race at the Empire City horse-track in New York, an achievement which gave him

By 1908, Oldfield had tired of the fairgrounds and announced his retirement, but the following year saw his return with a German Benz, a 120 hp model. In 1910, another Benz—the 200 hp Blitzen model—was used by Oldfield to establish new one-mile, two-mile and kilometre records at Ormond Beach. Even Kaiser Wilhelm sent his congratulations from Germany.

Because of his participation in unsanctioned match-races, Oldfield was often under suspension by the American Automobile Association and therefore was ineligible for major road races such as the Indianapolis 500 which was inaugurated in 1911. Late in 1912, however, his suspension was lifted and he was invited to take the late David Bruce-Brown's seat in the Fiat team for the annual Grand Prize at Milwaukee; Oldfield accepted and finished fourth.

The Mercer team signed Barney to drive for them in 1913 (although Mercer's team captain, Ralph DePalma, was angry and walked out) and

against the might of the all-conquering French teams. In the 1915 500, he withdrew his Bugatti as it was not quick enough, and the following year he was fifth in a Delage.

Other successes included second place in the 1914 Vanderbilt Cup driving a Mercer, second with a Maxwell in the 1914 Corona road race, victory in a Stuz in the 1914 Cactus Derby (a 670-mile road race) and victory in the Venice road race of 1915 driving a Maxwell.

In 1917, too old for military service, Oldfield campaigned his final exhibition car, the *Green Dragon*. This was a Miller-engined device with an enclosed cockpit, and to add to the showmanship Oldfield used to drive it clad in a green leather outfit. He retired from racing in 1918 and formed the Oldfield Tire & Rubber Co which he sold to Firestone four years later; it became, in effect, Firestone's racing division.

Barney Oldfield had become a very rich businessman, but he lost heavily in the 1929 Wall

Above right: Barney Oldfield with the trade mark that made him known at all the tracks—the cigar in the side of the mouth
Above left: Barney with the much publicised *Golden Submarine*, that did exhibition runs. Note that cigar again!

nationwide acclaim. He toured the country giving exhibition runs and match races, although exactly how many of these were genuine is not known as he paid his 'opposition', and Bill Pickens, his manager, was in charge of the stop-watches. Showmanship was his theme and he became famous as an extrovert, cigar-chewing entertainer who used to shout to his fans, 'You know me, I'm Barney Oldfield!' He even played briefly in a theatre in a presentation titled *Vanderbilt Cup*, when he would rev up his racing car on stage on a treadmill and shower his audience with dirt to give a dusty road effect.

he finished second in a 445-mile road race at Santa Monica. Oldfield's love for stunt and exhibition races (including one against an air-craft) meant he rarely remained in a team for long, and in quick succession he moved from Mercer to Maxwell and then to Stutz. With a Stutz he was fifth in the Indianapolis 500, a seemingly poor position but a great performance

Street crash—reportedly in excess of $1,000,000 —and became virtually penniless. He appeared in a film about himself and also had ideas of breaking the land-speed record in a special 3000 bhp car to be built by Harry Miller, but this remained a dream. Oldfield ended his days as an automotive consultant and died in Beverly Hills on 6 October 1946. MK

A HORSE WITHOUT THE SMELL

Ransom Olds was determined to build
an alternative to the horse

Above: in 1899,
Ransom Eli Olds and
S. L. Smith founded the
Olds Motor Works. Their
first product was a car
that has become famous
in the history of
American motor
manufacturing, the
'curved dash'
Oldsmobile; it was
powered by a single-
cylinder engine of 1563
cc and weighed 700 lb.
The car sold for $650

Above right: one of
Olds' earlier attempts at
producing an auto-
mobile, the 1897 Olds
motor wagon

YOUNG RANSOM ELI OLDS did not like the smell of horses
on the farm, so he decided to invent an automobile.
That was in the early 1880s, when Ransom was in his
early 20s. Born in 1864, he was the son of Pliny Fisk
Olds, a village mechanic in Geneva, north Ohio, not
far from Cleveland. Cleveland was already a major
engineering centre, with iron and steel manufacture,
farm implement production, oil-refining and ship-
building industries firmly established; and it was here
that Ransom went to school.

His father encouraged him to tinker with machinery
almost as soon as the boy was big enough to grasp a
spanner, and Ransom soon became a proficient
mechanic.

Pliny Olds eventually moved to Lansing, state
capital of Michigan, where he established an engineering shop on River Street. Young Ransom's role in the
household economy was to get up at five o'clock, light
the two household fires, and then walk down to the
workshop and fire up the boiler in the adjoining lean-to
which provided the power for the steam engine. Then
he went home for breakfast, attended school, and at
four o'clock was back working in the machine shop.
He spent all day Saturday, and all his holidays, in the

shop, for two years quite unpaid, and thereafter for
fifty cents a day.

The result of this hard training was that by the time
Ransom had finished high school, he had become an
expert machinist, and was proficient in pattern-making
and moulding. When he started to build engines in the
little lean-to beside the Olds barn, the neighbours
began to prophesy that no good would come of it.
'That kid of yours will blow his head off one day,
Pliny,' they forecast; but Ransom survived unscathed.
Indeed he was abetted in his experiments by his father,
and together they began to develop a crude internal
combustion engine based on the Otto stationary unit.

Ransom was now 21, and had bought himself a half-
share in the family business, paying his father his $300
savings and a promissory note for $800 at 8 per cent
interest.

'At the time I went in with him,' Ransom Olds
recalled 40 years later, 'Father's work consisted mainly
of repairing, but I wanted to manufacture, and it
seemed to me that we could create a demand for small
steam engines. We gradually worked out plans for a
small engine or boiler of one or two horsepower, which
could be operated by an ordinary stove burner. But
there was so much deposit in the river water that the
small boilers filled up with mud and were not very
satisfactory. Next I invented a gasoline motor which
was the first manufactured in the United States to use
gasoline directly in the cylinder. We made this up as
high as twelve to eighteen horsepower.'

Like most American pioneers, Olds was apt to pre-
date his early experiments, so his claim to have built
an internal-combustion car in 1886 must be regarded
with more than a modicum of suspicion. According to
B. C. Forbes, who interviewed Olds in 1925, the
vehicle 'was crude, built as it was from the various
parts he had been able to pay for out of his careful
savings. The body was made of whitewood, the frame
was substantially built of oak, and this somewhat
ungainly structure rested on three, steel-tyred buggy
wheels of conventional size.'

'What troubled him most,' said Forbes, 'was the
transmission, for its construction was crude indeed.

The rear axle had a ratchet on each side, and it was steered by an iron lever. The main drive wheel was an iron wheel with half-inch pointed pins screwed into the face to make a sprocket. The driving chain, made of strap iron, with rollers on pins to hold the links together, was operated through a set of lathe gears—the transmission! Unfortunately, there was no transmission case, and when the car was run the wood supports for the gears magnified the noise like a sounding board.

'When young Olds ran his motor vehicle out on the street in the early morning, the terrific noise of the gears shattered the peaceful silence and aroused the entire neighbourhood. Within five minutes, his progress had caused so much excitement that he decided a few hundred feet was sufficient for the first exhilerating tryout. . . .'

But one wonders how Ransom Olds had any spare time at all for experimenting with horseless carriages in 1886, for the family machine shop was in trouble. They had put up a small factory in the hope of increased sales of their gas engines, but in doing so had exhausted their finances—and attracted some customers who were incapable of paying for the goods

Top left: another example of the 'curved dash' Oldsmobile; this is a 1903 model and is on display in the Egeskov Veteran Museum in Denmark

Top right: the 'curved dash' Oldsmobile in action

Above: superbly restored, this 1902 'curved dash' runabout can be seen in the Lucerna Transport Museum

they had ordered. The Olds had to borrow as much as they were able, in an effort to rebuild the business.

'But in all that time I never lost faith in my idea of gasoline locomotion,' claimed Ransom Olds. 'All through those months I spent every spare minute tinkering with engines and experimenting with different forms of combustion. That little gasoline engine I had invented sold so well that it finally pulled us out of the hole and it convinced me more than ever that mechanical power as applied to all our regular functions was the coming solution of big business.'

Possibly much of that bold statement was romanticised hindsight, for it took three years to get the company back on its feet; and by then it was obvious that Pliny Olds was on the way out. Perhaps young Ransom's expansionist ideas frightened him; whatever the reason, when the Olds Gasoline Engine Works Incorporated was launched in 1890 with a capital of $30,000, Ransom Olds was made president and general manager. Within two years, he had entirely bought out his father's share in the business. Already engines were being shipped from coast to coast, and quite an export trade was built up with Great Britain.

By then Ransom Olds had built and run his first authentic motor vehicle. This was a three-wheeled steam car with a flash boiler, which attracted sufficient attention for the august *Scientific American* to despatch a correspondent to Lansing to write a feature on the vehicle. Olds told the reporter: 'It never kicks or bites, never tires on long runs, and never sweats in hot weather. It does not require care in the stable and only eats while on the road.' This article eventually found its way to India, whence Olds received an offer for his vehicle, and it was duly shipped overseas, the first-ever export by the American motor industry.

Around 1895, Olds began work on a gasoline buggy, with high wheels running on $1\frac{1}{2}$ in rubber tyres; the engine was mounted on the reach bars which linked the front and rear axles into one unsprung unit. In typical American buggy fashion, the dog-cart body wavered around above the axles on its own full-elliptic springs.

It probably made its first test runs in December 1895, for Olds recalled that the car was not ready at the

time of the *Chicago Times-Herald* race on November 28 that year.

By 1896 the car was a regular feature on the streets of Lansing, where it attracted the attention of a local capitalist named E. W. Sparrow, who persuaded two friends living in Detroit, S. L. Smith and Henry Russel, to join him in backing Olds to produce horseless carriages. Between them, they subscribed $50,000, and the Olds Motor Vehicle Company was founded; it was decided to locate the factory in Detroit, as Lancing was then a town of under 2000 inhabitants, with unpaved streets, while Detroit was an expanding industrial centre, with a rate of growth second only to Chicago, and a population of 205,876, which made it America's 14th largest city.

Notwithstanding its title, the company made very few motor vehicles in its new home on East Jefferson Avenue; its specialities were stationary gas and petrol engines, with marine power units a profitable sideline. Car manufacture was not seriously considered until 1899, when S. L. Smith, who had made his fortune in copper and lumber, decided to take over the company so that his two sons could have a lucrative hobby.

So he put up $199,600 and took 95 per cent of the stock: Ransom Olds chipped in $400 for the remaining 5 per cent, and was appointed president and general manager, though the former title was obviously only a courtesy one.

The Olds Motor Works was launched with grandiose schemes to build a $1250 luxury car with such advanced features as pneumatic clutch, cushion tyres, and electric push-button starter, but at that stage of the game the car-buying public regarded innovations of this kind—with complete justification—as the prime ingredients of mechanical failure, and the car failed to sell to such an extent that 1900 saw the Olds company running at a loss of $80,000.

At this point, Ransom Olds had the proverbial blinding flash of inspiration: 'After a long, sleepless

night, I decided to discard all my former plans and build a little one-cylinder runabout, for I was convinced that if success came it must be through a more simple machine. The plans which had formulated in my mind were very clear. It was my idea to build a machine which would weigh around 500 pounds and would sell for around $500. The result was the curved-dash 'Oldsmobile', weighing 700 pounds and selling at $650. My whole idea in building it was to have the operation so simple that anyone could run it and the construction such that it could be repaired at any local shop.'

In 1901, the prototype was ready, and the blueprints had all been drawn up ready for production: Olds had been working day and night to develop the new model, a little buggy whose toboggan-like body was perched on two long springs which served the dual function of locating the front and rear axles and acting as auxiliary chassis sidemembers. The single-cylinder engine displaced 1563 cc and drove the back axle through a

Top: the fabulous Limited model Oldsmobile of 1910 had an 11 ft 6 in wheelbase and was powered by a six-cylinder, 11,569 cc motor. One of these cars raced the 20th Century Limited railway express from New York to Albany and won— hence the name Limited. The model photographed can be seen in the Harrah Museum in America

Above: the six-cylinder model 53 of 1913

chain via a two-speed epicyclic transmission unit.

Then came instant disaster! A workman pulled his forge fire too close to a rubber gasbag which was being used to fuel one of the factory's engines, and the inevitable terrific explosion resulted. The factory, which was almost certainly principally built of clapboard, burst into flames, and the upstairs staff barely had time to save themselves, let alone bother about looking for blueprints. Within an hour, there was nothing left but scorched ruins—and the prototype runabout, which had been saved by a young timekeeper at the factory named James J. Brady who, hearing the explosion, had rushed to the section of the factory where the model was stored, and persuaded the staff to help him push the car out into the open.

tion as quickly as possible, and the Detroit automobile component industry was born.

They ordered engines and transmissions from the Dodge brothers, John and Horace, and further engines were supplied by Leland & Faulconer (though these were built to more precise standards than the Dodge units and showed up the engineering deficiencies of the Oldsmobile chassis).

The little Oldsmobile was an instant success. Pre-production models were used to test market reaction, and proved so popular that the decision was made to stake everything on this car: and the gamble proved an outstanding success. Some 600 Oldsmobiles were sold in 1901, and Olds then staggered the industry by announcing that he planned to build 4000 cars the

With supreme resilience, they started again from scratch. The car was taken apart, new blueprints were drawn from the parts, and work began on duplicates. At that time Olds was ill in hospital; within a month, the first 'duplicate' Oldsmobile was driven up to his ward window to assure him that all was well.

At that time the Olds company was a considerable reservoir of talent: among its staff were Charles Brady King, who had built Detroit's first car in 1896, Jonathan D. Maxwell, formerly with the Apperson brothers, Robert C. Hupp (who would later found Hupmobile) and two young University of Michigan graduates, Roy D. Chapin and Howard E. Coffin, who would go on to launch the Hudson car in 1909.

These varied skills were interwoven to make the Oldsmobile America's first successful mass-production petrol car—though like many other American mass-producers, Oldsmobile didn't manufacture all the components themselves. Indeed, it was essential for them to sub-contract in order to get into produc-

Above: an advert for the 1927 Oldsmobile 'Six' coach sedan showing the car in a very English setting. Note the size of the car in relation to the passengers who are dressed in typical American 'Jazz Age' clothes

following year. In fact, output for 1902 was 2500, but that was more than enough to silence those who had thought that there would not be sufficient demand for cars to support such outputs.

One reason for the popularity of the little car was a well-publicised 820-miles-in-seven-days endurance run from Detroit to the New York Automobile Show by Roy Chapin (though by all accounts the breakdown-fraught journey proved the driver's endurance rather than the car's); Olds talked one major New York firm, A. G. Spalding & Company, into ordering 100 cars and taking an agency, but they soon cancelled the order after a directors' meeting had agreed that there was no chance of selling as many as 100 cars in New York City.

Then, however, the Cleveland agent for Oldsmobile, R. M. Owen, wandered on to the stand with his backer, Roy Rainey, and announced that sales had been so good that Rainey was interested in starting another agency for Owen, in New York. They proposed ordering 500 cars, but Ransom Olds commented: 'Why not make it a thousand cars, boys, and get some notice?'

Rainey and Owen agreed, and a contract was signed the same night.

Their publicity campaign seems to have been crude, cheap and effective: They started out by doing stunts with the cars on Fifth Avenue to attract attention. They got themselves arrested for speeding, upset a bicycle policeman, and made the car so talked about that people began to look into the matter seriously. That year 750 cars were sold in New York City, and the factory had to announce a waiting list.

Soon, too, the little tiller-steered Oldsmobile became the first car to be immortalised in a popular song: 'Come with me Lucille in my Merry Oldsmobile' crooned the harmony songsters of the day. The tune, written by Gus Edwards and Vincent Bryan, was re-recorded in the 1920s as a giveaway gimmick for a new Oldsmobile model by the Jean Goldkette Band with Bix Beiderbecke on cornet, and this waxing is now one of the rarest jazz collectors' items in existence, less than half-a-dozen copies having survived.

The best thing, though, about the Oldsmobile was that it was designed for the non-mechanically minded customer, for whom the instruction booklet was suitably reassuring: 'Don't confess that you are less intelligent than thousands of people who are driving Oldsmobiles. We make the only motor that 'motes'. . . . Don't drive your Oldsmobile more than 100 miles on the first day. You wouldn't drive a green horse ten

Above: an Oldsmobile 33 convertible coupé of 1933. Two extra passengers could be carried in the 'dickey' or 'rumble' seat behind the driver

Below: a parade of American cars led by a 1932 Oldsmobile convertible coupé

miles till you were acquainted with him. Do you know more about a gasoline motor than you do about a horse?'

By applying cycle industry methods of standardisation and production, Olds was able to step up output of his gas buggy on an impressive scale. At the Detroit Automobile and Sportsmen's Show in early 1903, he announced that the car had ceased to be a luxury, and had now become a utility. Within ten years, he predicted, the average car would weigh 700–800 lb and be small, compact and simply constructed. As if to prove him right, sales of Oldsmobiles rose to 4000 for the

year, and the Oldsmobile works was claimed to be the world's biggest automobile factory. Engines were still supplied by the Dodges and Leland and Faulconer, bodies by the C. R. Wilson Body Company on Cass Avenue—both the latter companies were soon also supplying the newly founded Ford Motor Company.

The Oldsmobile assembly process, which used jigs and machine tools to build up the complete vehicles in progressive steps was the first tentative step of the motor industry towards the moving production line. *Automobile* wrote in December 1903: 'The motors are passed, step by step, down the assembling bench towards the testing department which is in the next room, a new piece being added at every move with clocklike regularity.'

A few months later, the Detroit *Free Press* visited the Olds Motor Works: 'Rows upon rows of special

Below: the advertising blurb for this 1936–7 Eight Sport Coupé reads '... The all-weather coupé "that has everything!" Interior matches exterior Oldsmobile streamline beauty. Fisher No Draft Ventilation and the solid-steel "Turret-Top" Body by Fisher. The friends who go along? Always comfortable in that wide and roomy rumble seat'. There is not much one can say after that!

machinery are humming and buzzing away, bewildering the onlooker with their number. A great expanse of floor space stretches away before the visitor, along which are arranged these ingenious devices, each with its own peculiar work to do. Some bore out the cylinders, each machine making two cylinders at a time; some finish the connecting rods and shafts; in fact every step in the process of turning out the finished machinery of a modern car is carried out by a group of these beautiful machines. The finishing and enamelling of the bodies, the upholstery of seats and cushions, and so on, are carried on in a large separate part of the plant. One little imagines, as he looks at the swiftly running car on the street, the immense amount of detail and careful manipulation that have been necessary on the hundreds of parts before they have all been brought together and adjusted to form this engine of commerce and pleasure.'

Sales in 1904 reached 5000, but Ransom Olds was soon given cause to remember that he owned only 5 per cent of the company, for Samuel Smith decided that it was time the company (of which son Fred was now secretary and treasurer) ought to be getting into the lucrative field of high-powered luxury cars. Which was not at all what Ransom Olds wanted, so he decided it was time to retire. 'We had done so well by that time,' he recalled, 'that I thought I had about all that I needed, and rather than hamper the ideas of the rest of the group I sold out my stock and decided to take a long vacation.'

That was in August 1904; and while Olds was holidaying in Northern Michigan with his family, he received a telegram asking him to return to Lansing.

'As I stepped off the train, I was met by an old friend who handed me an interesting looking paper. Reading it, I found that a group of my friends had

organised a half-million dollar company, of which I was to be the head, and within three hours had raised the money to finance it. Of this, I was to have a controlling interest, $260,000.' And thus the Reo was born, and at first built vehicles of a fairly similar type to the Oldsmobile.

Soon the rival companies were neighbours, for in the summer of 1905, Samuel Smith, attracted by the offer of a 52-acre site subscribed for by the Lansing Businessmen's Association, decided to move Oldsmobile back to its (and his) home town.

As yet, there was little divergence from the pattern laid down by Ransom Olds. The standard 'curved-dash' model was still available, with its tiller steering that enabled tyro drivers to determine which way the front wheels were pointing; but now there was also a 'Touring Runabout' version with wheel steering and a dummy bonnet, priced at $750, plus a 20 hp flat-twin model with five-seated touring coachwork, which cost $1400. There was also a 'Coach', a forward-control 11-seated shooting brake-type vehicle, with a 16 hp vertical-twin engine; this vehicle cost $2200.

The Curved-dash Olds was still listed the following year, but it now looked a poor old-fashioned thing, and was available at no extra cost with 'straight-dash' bodywork, a futile attempt at updating. There were two new car models, the Model L 'Double-Action Olds', and the 26/28 hp Model S.

The Double-Action had a vertical-twin two-stroke engine of 20/24 hp rating, and like the Model S, broke new ground for this marque by adopting a three-speed sliding-gear transmission and a shaft-driven rear axle; it cost $1250 complete with four-seated coachwork.

The Model S, priced at $2250, had a four-cylinder engine, the company's first, while for lovers of the grandiose there was an 18-seated wagonette with a horrifying rear overhang, for which Oldsmobile considered the old 16 hp vertical-twin and two-speed epicyclic transmission were still adequate.

This ambitious marketing programme was pushed through despite the advice of Roy Chapin, who had taken over as sales manager in 1904, and raised the output of Runabouts to 6500 in 1905; and the high-priced models began to build up losses. Equally, though, the Runabout was clearly on the wane. Fred Smith was a great one for inventing slogans for the Oldsmobile Runabout, and had coined the phrase, 'Nothing to watch but the road'. 'The idea is good,' commented an owner, who was obviously fed up with the glacier-like performance of his Oldsmobile, 'but I get darned tired of watching the same piece of road.'

By early 1906, Oldsmobile was in debt, its cash reserves depleted. Roy Chapin and his friend Howard Coffin (Oldsmobile's newly-appointed chief engineer) were among those who resigned at this time.

But the company continued with its Alice-in-Wonderland bigger-and-bigger production pro-gramme in the face of convincing financial proof of the total error of such a course. 1908 saw the introduction

Top: the two-door Oldsmobile 70 of 1938 was powered by an eight-cylinder engine and was regarded as a somewhat prestige model by the public

Above: a 1954 Oldsmobile two-door convertible

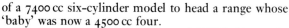

of a 7400 cc six-cylinder model to head a range whose 'baby' was now a 4500 cc four.

The inevitable takeover that year left Billy Durant in charge, and Oldsmobile one of the less healthy components of the new General Motors group, a position that was not helped by the new management's insistence on repeating all the mistakes of the Smith regime on an even bigger scale. A truly colossal car appeared in 1910 in the shape of an 11,569 cc six, which carried its 11 ft 6 in wheelbase aloft on 42 in wheels, which gave the car such vertiginous height that a double-stepped running-board was essential. One of these cars raced the famous 20th Century Limited railway express from New York to Albany—and won—after which the model took the name *Limited* in honour of the event, though 'unlimited' might have been more appropriate.

After 1912, however, there were reassuring signs that the days of the behemoths were numbered, for the biggest in the range was now a mere baby of 6997 cc; refinements such as compressed-air starters and four-speed transmissions were available, while Delco electric starting and lighting were standardised in 1914.

A low-priced four was added to the range in 1915, to be joined in 1916 by a 4-litre V8 which combined low cost with high efficiency; its side-valve engine had aluminium pistons, a definite innovation at that period.

The 1916 season saw Oldsmobile produce the millionth General Motors car, one of their new 2900 cc sixes; but after the Armistice the V8 was the prime offering, though a stop-gap ohv four using the same 2.8-litre engine as its sister marque, Chevrolet, was launched in 1921, only to be swept away, like the V8, in 1923.

The one model which replaced them was a 2774 cc six with a Buick-like radiator, which was intended to appeal to a slightly 'sportier' class of customer than other GM marques attracted.

'The impulse to sit behind its wheel, step on the accelerator and drive out into the open—through valleys, up steep hills and to buck up against most any obstacle of travel seems to come with the first view of the Oldsmobile Sport Touring,' carolled the sales literature.

'Some manufacturers have neglected their open cars and cater principally to closed-car buyers. But not so with Oldsmobile, who, realising that there are many who prefer open-car freedom, has kept abreast of the times with fine appointments of comfort, beauty and convenience in the Touring Car. . . . The Touring Car is beautiful and graceful from all angles. Its body is hung close to the ground and passengers enjoy comfort from sitting down deep in the cushions rather than on them. . . . Performance—fleetness of acceleration when in traffic, or starting from a standstill, and power that virtually removes the hills from the highways—is in such abundance in this latest Oldsmobile Six that everyone who has driven it marvels at the reserve that seems ever ready to meet any demand. It fulfils every letter of the creed to which it was built—"Beauty, Performance, Price—Not one but all three".'

The year 1927 saw the marque pioneering the use of chromium-plated brightwork, and introducing four-wheel braking. Sales rose from 44,000 in 1924 to over 100,000 in 1929, in which year a low-priced V8, the Viking, was launched. It was based on the LaSalle, and had a 4244 cc sidevalve power unit, but the Depression was the wrong time to launch a V8, and within two years the Viking was dead.

But Oldsmobile were still multi-cylinder minded, as the announcement of a new 3933 cc straight-eight in 1932 bore witness. The company was gradually evolving into a corporate kite-flyer for new technical advances, though there was nothing specially advanced

Above left: front-end view of the 1951 Oldsmobile model

Top right: the two-door Oldsmobile 88 of 1954

Above: the conservative lines of the F-85 model of 1963 made a pleasant change from the extravagant styling that had been a feature of American cars only a few years earlier

about the adoption of independent front suspension in 1934. The following year saw the controversial 'Turret-top' styling, which hinted at the jellymould shapes of the future, while 1938 saw the first production General Motors automatic transmissions installed in Oldsmobiles. This transmission seems to have been beset with its share of troubles, for American historians point to 1940 as being of far greater significance, for in that year, they claim, the automatic became reliable.

And the Oldsmobile had always had a name for reliability, though in the post-war era the marque name was to be hung around the neck of some pretty weird styling exercises.

There were also the technical innovations, though whether all of these represented an advance in the automotive art is questionable: 'Autronic eye' automatic headlamp beam control, air conditioning, four-barrel carburettors. Many of them merely represented extra hefty chunks of electronic circuitry for the power unit to haul around, demanding a return to monster power units to maintain performance levels.

The year 1949 brought 'Futuramic' styling and a 4965 cc 'Rocket' V8, heralding the descent into the styling abyss followed by so many contemporary American marques, which plumbed bottom with such disasters as the 1958 Dynamic 88 Starfire Coupé (it was all Starfire and Jetfire in those days, though there

was the token attempt at building a compact, the 3523 cc V8 F-85 of 1961).

The old sporty image was revived with the 1962 Cutlass version of the F-85, while even more performance—110 mph—was promised the following year by a turbocharged Jetfire version of this car. It is perhaps hardly coincidental that the following year the V8 was shelved in favour of a Buick-based V6, while a range of Jetstar eights made further attempts at offering economy.

But the real breakthrough for Olds came in 1966, when they announced their first chain-drive model since the demise of the curved-dash runabout; but there could not have been a greater contrast between the two concepts, for the new Tornado used short silent-tooth chains to drive the front wheels—through Hydramatic transmission.

Not surprisingly, it was a big car, with a 6965 cc V8 engine, yet it aroused much acclaim at a time when technical innovation was apt to be sniped at with the old 'unsafe at any speed' parrot-cry of the Nader-raiders. Engine capacity was upped to 7456 cc in 1968.

It is perhaps appropriate that America's oldest motor manufacturing company should have passed its three-quarter century building such a distinctive machine, though one wonders what Ransom Olds (and, for that matter, Samuel Smith) would have thought of it.   DBW

Top left: the Oldsmobile Omega of 1973; note the unusual front-end styling

Top right: one of Oldsmobile's best-known models was the Toronado; this is the Custom version of 1972

Above left: the Omega hatchback coupé of 1973

Above right: the 1973 Cutlass Colonnade sedan

OMEGA

Following the trend of the other large American car manufacturers, Oldsmobile announced a small car in 1973: the Omega.

Two engines are available for the Omega, a 100 bhp, 4097 cc in-line six and a 180 bhp, 5736 cc V8. These engines are also used in other General Motors vehicles, such as Chevrolet and Buick. Two transmissions, a three-speed manual and a three-speed automatic, are available for the six-cylinder version, while the V8 can be acquired with only the Turbo-Hydramatic automatic unit.

The Omega uses an integral body/chassis unit, with an additional front sub-frame, and has independent front suspension by means of wishbones, coil springs, an anti-roll bar and telescopic dampers. The rear suspension is by a rigid axle, semi-elliptic leaf springs and telescopic dampers.

Three body styles are available for the car: a two-door coupé, a three-door hatchback coupé and a four-door saloon. As for performance, the six-cylinder models have a top speed of 99 mph, while the

V8s can reach a speed of 118 mph. The six-cylinders use a gallon of petrol for every 15.3 miles, and the V8s return 14.5 miles for every gallon they use.

As is usual with American cars, many options of trim are available, as well as extras such as air-conditioning, heated rear window and front disc brakes with servo-assistance. A power-assisted steering is optional; this means that you get a higher-geared system than with the manual, which, by the way, needs no less than 5.65 wheel turns to get it from lock to lock.

ENGINE Front-mounted, water-cooled straight-six or V8. 98.2 mm (3.87 in) bore × 89.6 mm (3.53 in) stroke = 4097 cc (250 cu in) (6-cylinder versions), or 103.1 mm (4.06 in) bore × 85.8 mm (3.38 in) stroke = 5736 cc (350 cu in) (V8-cylinder versions). Maximum power (DIN) 100 bhp at 3600 rpm (6), or 180 bhp at 3800 rpm (V8); maximum torque (DIN) 175 lb ft at 1800 rpm (6), or 275 lb ft at 2800 rpm (V8). Cast-iron cylinder block and head(s). Compression ratio 8.5:1 (both

models). 7 main bearings (6), or 5 main bearings (V8). 2 valves per cylinder operated, via push-rods and rockers, by a single camshaft, side mounted (6), or at centre of V (V8). 1 Rochester downdraught single-barrel carburettor (6), or 1 Rochester downdraught four-barrel carburettor (V8).

TRANSMISSION Single-dry-plate clutch and three-speed manual gearbox, or torque converter and three-speed automatic. Ratios for manual 1st 2.450, 2nd 1.500, 3rd 1, rev 2.630:1. Ratios for automatic 1st 2.520, 2nd 1.520, 3rd 1, rev 1.930:1. Hypoid-bevel final drive. Ratio 3.080 (6, optional on 8), or 2.730 (V8).

CHASSIS Integral with front sub-frame.

SUSPENSION Front—independent by wishbones, coil springs, an anti-roll bar and telescopic dampers. Rear—non independent by a rigid axle, semi-elliptic leaf springs and telescopic dampers.

STEERING Recirculating ball,

servo optional. Turns from lock to lock 5.65.

BRAKES Drum all round. Servo assistance and front discs optional.

WHEELS 5 in × 14 in steel.

TYRES E78 × 14.

DIMENSIONS AND WEIGHT Wheelbase 111 in; track—front 59.10 in, rear—58.80 in; length 199.50 in; width 72.80 in; height 52.40 in (coupés), or 53.80 in (saloon); ground clearance 4.90 in; dry weight (six-cylinder version) 3438 lb (hatchback coupé), 3334 lb (coupé), or 3382 lb (saloon). For V8s, add 221 lb; turning circle between walls 41.2 ft; fuel tank capacity 17.6 gals.

BODY 2-door coupé, 3-door hatchback coupé and 4-door saloon. All have 6 seats.

PERFORMANCE Maximum speed 99 mph (6-cylinder versions), or 118 mph (V8 versions). Fuel consumption 15.3 mpg (6-cylinder), or 14.5 mpg (V8).

TORONADO

At the top end of the Oldsmobile range is the company's flagship, the Toronado, although most people mispronounce it and instead say Tornado.

Probably the most unusual feature of the Toronado is that its front wheels are turned by a torque converter and automatic gearbox, chain driven from the engine. The car's power unit is a 230 bhp, 7456 cc engine that can propel the 4838 lb machine to a top speed of 124 mph. The price one has to pay for such performance in a heavyweight car is a fuel consumption that averages out at 11.8 mpg.

Based on a channel-section perimeter-type frame, this Oldsmobile has independent front suspension by wishbones, longitudinal torsion bars, an anti-roll bar and telescopic dampers. The rear suspension is non independent by a rigid axle, lower trailing radius arms, upper oblique

torque arms, coil springs and telescopic dampers.

Braking is taken care of by servo-assisted front discs (with radial fins) and rear drums. Power-assisted steering, with 3.24 turns from lock to lock, directs the vehicle.

The two-door Toronado coupé has bench seats in the front, which means the car can carry up to six people. Options available for the car are electronic ignition, a tilting steering wheel, a heavy-duty cooling system, air conditioning and a Brougham interior.

ENGINE Front-mounted, water-cooled V8. 104.8 mm (4.13 in) bore × 107.9 mm (4.25 in) stroke = 7456 cc (455 cu in). Maximum power 230 bhp at 3800 rpm; maximum torque 370 lb ft at 2800 rpm. Cast-iron cylinder block and heads. Compression ratio 8.5:1. 5 main bearings.

2 valves per cylinder operated, via pushrods and rockers, by a single camshaft at the centre of the V. 1 Rochester 4MC down-draught four-barrel carburettor.

TRANSMISSION Torque converter and three-speed automatic gearbox. Maximum ratio of converter at stall × 2. Ratios 1st 2.480, 2nd 1.480, 3rd 1, rev 2.080:1. Spiral-bevel final drive. Ratio 2.730:1 (optional 3.070:1).

CHASSIS Channel-section perimeter-type frame.

SUSPENSION Front—independent by wishbones, longitudinal torsion bars, an anti-roll bar and telescopic dampers. Rear—non independent by a rigid axle, lower trailing radius arms, upper oblique torque arms, coil springs and telescopic dampers.

STEERING Servo-assisted recircu-

lating ball. Turns from lock to lock 3.24.

BRAKES Power-assisted discs front (with internal radial fins) and rear drums.

WHEELS 6 in × 15 in steel.

TYRES J78 × 15 (standard), or JR78 × 15 (optional).

DIMENSIONS AND WEIGHT Wheelbase 122 in; track—front 63.50 in, rear—63.60 in; length 228 in; width 79.50 in; height 53.30 in; ground clearance 5.60 in; dry weight 4838 lb; turning circle between walls 46.6 ft; fuel tank capacity 26.1 gals.

BODY 2-door, 6-seat (2 bench seats) coupé.

PERFORMANCE Maximum speed 124 mph. Fuel consumption 11.8 mpg.

NEVER WHAT IT SEEMED

OM cars were different things to different people. In Italy they were regarded as tourers that performed like sports cars while in Britain they *were* sports cars

Right: an OM type 465 competing in the Coppa del Alpi of 1922. The 465 was fitted with a four-cylinder, 1327 cc engine developing a modest 18 bhp. The car, however, was very light and handled extremely well, features which proved very popular with the motoring public

ONLY THE MOST INCURABLE of romantics could pretend that automobile design today is anything other than a science, or at least a technology. In the 1920s, however, it was still an art: that is to say, much of it was arbitrary and subjective, because much of it was not properly understood. Because of this, manufacturers used to come on the scene and disappear again after brief and sometimes disastrous experiments with a market that was equally ignorant but not at all forgiving; and of those manufacturers who stayed longer, it was usual for them to present a rapid succession of new models— like the operatic tenor whose Italian audience insisted that he do encore after encore in the hope, as one of them put it, that he would eventually get it right. Very occasionally, however, a car would come on the market that was right from the beginning, and then it would remain in production for years and years, with very little development until time and changing standards made it no longer acceptable, when it would be found that the management and designers had forgotten what was required of them. The OM was one of these—in Italy at least; but in Britain, where it was also popular, it underwent a great deal of development and modification by its importers, and the little coterie of English enthusiasts for the make carried on buying these 'concessionaire's specials' for some years after the cars had gone out of production in their homeland.

The OM company was formed in Milan in 1899, representing the merger of two firms in the railways business, one of them making locomotives and the other rolling stock. Their first departure from this field was to make tramcars, Italy's first, which ran between Firenze and Fiesole. It was a rational step for a firm that recognised the increasing variety of mechanised transport; and the logical next step, car manufacture, was encompassed in 1918 by their acquisition of the Züst company which had been making big touring cars since 1905.

The first Züsts were very much in the Mercédès idiom, and were successful enough to prompt the Milanese firm to set up a new factory in Brescia (hence Brixia-Züst, from the Latin name for the city) until with their market success fading, they relied entirely on the Brescia works, where their last new model was produced in 1913. This was a 4.7-litre car known as the S305, with monobloc engine in Fiat style, and a 60 mph performance that its rear-wheel brakes could hardly match. This was the car that OM acquired with the Züst company, and it remained in production until 1923. It was improved to suit the times, with electrical equipment being added, for example; but it was hardly competitive with the attractive machines being produced by the company's rivals in Italy, and the directors demanded a new car. To design it they employed an Austrian named Barratouché, who produced a car with the twin virtues of essential simplicity and scope for considerable future development. The engine was a very plain-looking side-valve four-cylinder affair, with a cast-iron block on a light-alloy crankcase; but the cylinder head was detachable and the crankshaft ran in three main bearings at a time when two were thought ample, the centre main being water-cooled. The piston stroke was 100 mm, and this was to remain a constant in subsequent models; the bore was 65, and this with the number of cylinders gave the car its type number 465. Arithmetic gave it a displacement of 1327 cc, and the dynamometer gave it a figure of 18 bhp as a modest boast, on a par with the $1\frac{1}{2}$-litre Fiat 501 that was so popular.

Although its basic features were so terribly ordinary, the 465 revealed a good deal of loving care in its detailing. The cooling might be by thermosyphon, the draught assisted by a wooden-bladed fan, but the electrics were 12V with coil ignition by Bosch, and there was extensive use of light alloys not only in the engine but also the transmission and the main chassis bulkhead. Light weight was in fact one of the cornerstones of Barratouché's design: the connecting rods were machined all over, the chassis was formed from thin channel sections, and the rear axle even sought efficiency at the expense of noise by the use of straight-cut bevels for the final drive. The wheels were centre-lock wire-spoked types, but on the other hand all four had brakes. Just as important, the standard open four-seater tourer body was light and well proportioned so as not to upset the inherently good balance of the chassis, which soon proved that the OM was a delight to drive even though not blessed with a very high performance. Its roadworthiness enabled it to win the Coppa del

Garda in 1920, and to take second place in the general classification as well as a class win in the same event two years later. By this time, however, the want of power had been remedied to some extent: in 1921 a bore enlargement made it the type 467, and in the following year the 469 became a full $1\frac{1}{2}$-litre affair that was to be a success in Italian sports-car competition.

By the end of 1923 one of the major developments implicit in Barratouché's original design was ready for production. This was the simple addition of another two cylinders to make the type 665, a two-litre car that dealt fairly finally with objections about lack of performance. It was still a side-valve engine, and ought not

Below left: now to be seen in the Turin Automobile Museum is this example of OM's 665 NV model of 1931

Below right: drivers Morandi and Minoia posing with their OM 2000 prior to the start of the 1927 Mille Miglia which they won

Bottom: the lovely OM 665 sports model was powered by a six-cylinder 2200 cc engine fitted with a Roots supercharger

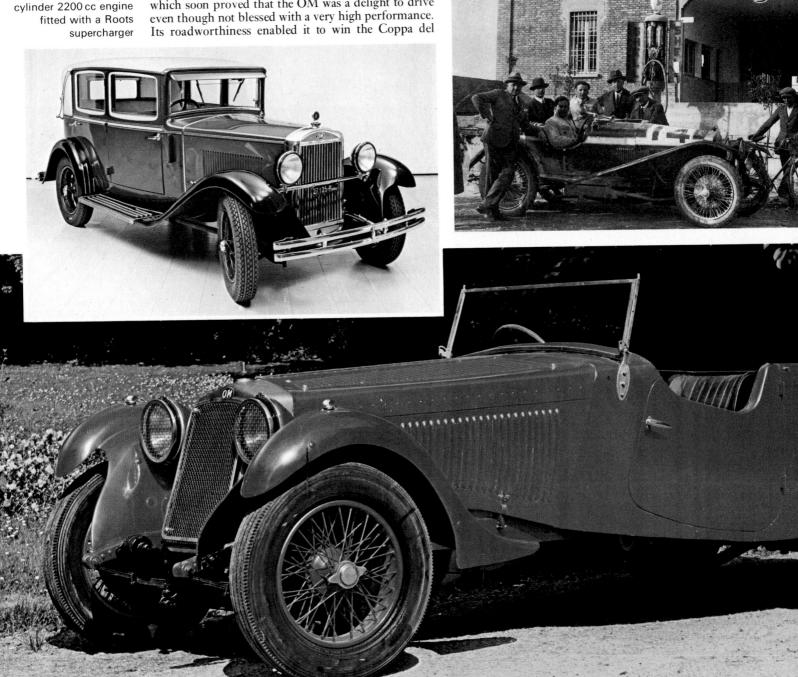

to have been competitive with the numerous OHV machines being produced by doughty opponents in Italy, Britain and elsewhere; but on the other hand, the complete car was still beautifully light (only 16½ cwt) and superbly balanced, with steering of the finger and thumb variety and predictability in handling of a high order. There seemed nothing to cavil at in its reliability, either: the extension of the crankshaft called merely for another main bearing, water-cooled like the original central one of the four-cylinder engine; and so long as it stayed beneath the limits imposed by the three-per-revolution torsional flutter of an inline six-throw crankshaft, the four-bearing OM component had the smooth running characteristics typical of such engines up to crankshaft rates that were fairly high by the standards of the time. Peak power was developed at

Below: the OM 469 model was introduced in 1922 and continued in production until 1929; it was fitted with a 1½-litre four-cylinder engine

opposition from various French makes was considered sterner than what was anticipated from Britain's three-litre Bentley and Sunbeam teams. At any rate the cars did respectably, dead-heating for fourth place at an average speed of 53.34 mph, about 4 mph slower than the winning 3½-litre Lorraine Dietrich. The following year two OMs ran at Le Mans again, winning the Rudge-Whitworth Cup and finishing fourth and fifth —again at a respectable distance behind the Lorraine Silken Six. 1927 was the great year for the two-litre OM, however, for this was the year that saw the birth of the Mille Miglia. It was almost an OM procession: the winning car was driven by Minoia and Morandi at an average speed of 40.27 mph, to be followed by two other factory-prepared cars of the same type. The following year OM would take first eight places in the

4200 rpm, and the engine was happy enough up to 4500—quite enough for a side-valver. With a single carburettor it gave only 40 bhp in its original form, but this output was soon increased by 50%; and a twin-carburettor cylinder block, believed to have been designed at the same time as the original car, later came on the scene to endow the two-litre OM with even higher performance. Sporting-bodied varieties could reach 75 mph, and maintain relatively high averages because of their excellent cornering and handling, not to mention the brisk acceleration that was as much a function of the car's low weight as of anything else.

This was the car that really made the OM famous in competition and popular in the market place. In 1925 it won the Tripoli Grand Prix, driven by Balestrero, took a class victory in the 12-hour touring car race at San Sebastian, and fifth place in the Targa Florio behind four Bugattis. Perhaps the most interesting entry that year was of two cars at Le Mans: their engine displacement was given as 2005 cc, an anomaly that has never been satisfactorily explained. It may be that the dèsaxé crankshaft location would have accounted for the difference in capacity between calculations based on the actual piston stroke, and those based on the crankshaft throw; it may, alternatively, be that the cars were deliberately overbored in order to take them out of the two-litre class where

two-litre class of the Mille Miglia, the best of them finishing second overall.

If a light touring car with a side-valve engine could fare so well in events of such status, what might not OM achieve with a purpose-built racer? They were tempted to try the idea for the 1926 season, but the car that emerged was a curiously half-baked affair. At that time the regulations governing Grand Prix racing dictated engines of not more than 1½-litres displacement, and OM therefore embarked upon a twin-overhead-camshaft straight eight in the best traditions expounded by Fiat, Alfa Romeo, and in that same year by Talbot and Delage. Perhaps it was a good engine, but the three-speed gearbox was an inexplicable handicap to it at a time when the little straight-eight Delage was making the most of—and demonstrating the need for—a five-speed gearbox. Worse still, the chassis created some handling problems that were not at all the sort of thing to which the OM factory drivers were accustomed. The car was entered for the French Grand Prix at Miramas, but did not start—a circumstance that brought no more disgrace upon OM than upon the numerous other manufacturers who treated this event in the same way, leaving it to Bugatti to win unopposed. In 1927, two Grand Prix OM straight eights were entered and did in fact start in the European Grand Prix, held at Monza. To cover 500 kilometres around that particular circuit demanded nothing very extravagant in the way of transmissions, nor did it make any great demands on the handling abilities of the cars: so although a Delage ran away to win, as happened in all but one of the year's important Grands Prix, an OM finished second, and another fourth, behind that other three-speed fish out of water, the Miller.

By this time the two-litre OM was finding a lot of enthusiastic customers in England. The enthusiasm was carefully nurtured into something a little short of an obsession by the British concessionaires, L. C. Rawlence & Company. For a start they retained Major R. F. Oats, previously notable for the improbable competition successes he scored in the little 11.9 horsepower Lagonda, to develop and race OMs in British events at Brooklands and elsewhere. Next they developed an astonishing range of high-performance conversion equipment, enabling them to market OMs the like of which were never seen in the OM catalogue. From 1926 there thus appeared two almost completely separate strains of OM cars, the standard machinery issued by the Brescia factory, and the extensively modified Rawlence hot-rods that were clearly intended to appeal to the known predilections of a carefully cultivated clientele. There were numerous variations in body style, from a simple two-seater to a long six-light Weymann saloon, but it was the mechanical options that were the most astonishing. There was a heavy duty ENV gearbox, a special Ricardo cylinder head with two spark plugs to each cylinder, and Dewandre servo operation of the brakes. Before long there was an overhead valve conversion with three carburettors as well as twelve spark plugs, and other variations included a low underslung chassis frame, a raked radiator, and special axle ratios—though by now OM had made a concession to modernity in fitting spiral bevel gears in their axles instead of the old straight-cut noisemakers.

Eventually the factory cottoned on to the possibilities still inherent in the 665 and started making their own high-performance versions. In 1929 they built some low-chassis cars with finned cylinder heads and Roots superchargers. These cars developed 80 bhp at 4000 rpm. The following year the capacity was increased to 2.2 litres, though the type number 665 was retained; and if the designation in the Rawlence catalogue was anything to go by, these blown sports versions developed 95 bhp. The factory went one better for its own team of sports racers, with three cars of 2.35 litres capacity. These were entered for the Irish

Below: like the OM cars, the OM factory at Brescia was modest but efficient. This photograph of the OM factory, taken in 1921, shows the front of the factory together with some unfinished OM products

Grand Prix and the Tourist Trophy to be held at Phoenix Park, Dublin, but the race ended disastrously for OM with the complete disappearance of the cars' brake linings which were of a new type. Within the confines of Italy the OMs were still a force with which to reckon; outside they seemed consistently unlucky.

In any case the Italian company was losing interest in car manufacture. It may be that they could foresee the coming of the slump that was to spell an end to the hopes of so many other manufacturers; it may simply be that the resurgence of Italy in political and economic terms was enough to prompt them to concentrate on truck manufacture, especially since OM had always been able to look to the Italian government for a worthwhile amount of business. It may be, too, that they recognised the impossibility of doing much more with a basic design that derived from 1920, and were not at all confident that if they were to try again they would be so lucky a second time.

Accordingly they began to run down the car business, as they built up their manufacture of commercial vehicles powered by Saurer diesels built under licence. It was a long drawn out business, not a little confusing in retrospect: the entire stock of private cars at the Brescia factory was sold in 1930 to a firm (run by two former OM management staff) called Esperia, yet in 1931 there was ostensibly a works entry for the Mille Miglia that netted a second place. In England things were even more extraordinary: no new cars were delivered to Rawlence after the end of 1930, and yet there were new models announced at the 1931 and 1933 Motor Shows at Olympia. Even in 1934 Rawlence showed something they called a 667 sports four-seater, but it was really a 1930 car, built (like so many of the other OMs delivered to English customers up to as late as 1935) from the big stock of spare parts stored underneath the railway arches at Waterloo.

In Italy, derivatives of the cars, designed as vans or taxis, remained in production for a little while alongside light military vehicles that saw service in World War II, but by 1933 any prospect of returning seriously to car manufacture was finally doomed by the sale of OM to Fiat. There was a rearguard action, based on a new car called the OMV or Alcyone, which was announced in 1934: it had overhead exhaust valves, a synchromesh gearbox and hydraulic brakes, but it never went into production. In 1975, OM still existed and played a significant part in the overall Fiat strategy, concentrating on lorries that, like the cars before them, were beautifully made and had an unexpectedly high performance.   LJKS

AN ILLUSION OF GRANDEUR

Ontario Motor Speedway was built to be the best circuit in the world; it never was

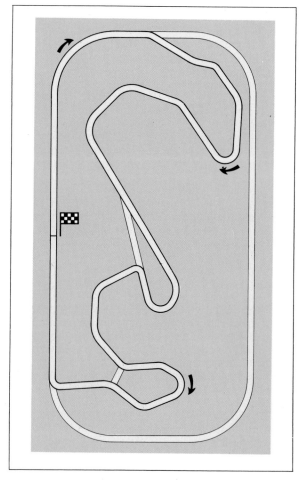

Right: the Ontario Motor Speedway complex is situated fairly near to Los Angeles, California, not in Canada, as its name would suggest

IT WAS TO HAVE BEEN the grandest motor racing project ever. Ignoring the pessimists, the founders of the Ontario Motor Speedway sought to make their circuit the envy of the world, a monument to motor racing which would elevate it to the top of all sports. History was to prove the founders wrong, but the circuit survives and operates today on a lesser scale than originally envisaged.

Ontario Motor Speedway is *not* in Canada. It is situated in California 40 miles east of Los Angeles near the airport in the city of Ontario. Work on the project was begun amid huge publicity on 9 July 1968. The 697-acre site was acquired for $5.8 million and it was planned to run the first race just over two years later in September 1970. Plans comprised a 2½-mile banked-turn super speedway, similar to Indianapolis but faster, a 3.194-mile road-racing circuit using part of the speedway plus an infield section and, lastly, a drag racing strip. Intended to be the most comprehensive racing complex ever, the specification included a seating capacity of 145,000 (95,000 permanent grandstand seats plus 45,000 portable seats), permanent rest rooms, garages, service buildings, a club house, restaurant, hospitality suites, parking for more than 50,000 vehicles, electronic scoreboard, two-level air-conditioned press room, etc.

In order to finance the project $25.5 million was raised by the Ontario Motor Speedway Corporation, a non-profit-making body which issued tax-free bonds offering 7½% interest. The bonds, held by around 970 individuals, were to mature on 1 February 1998, when the track would be assigned to the city of Ontario—although the city would not be liable for any debt should the Speedway run into financial problems meantime. In turn, the corporation leased the speedway to Ontario Motor Speedway Inc, a profit-orientated company capitalised with $500,000 in cash plus letters of credit totalling $1.5 million. OMS Inc had to pay an annual rent of $2 million to the corporation to cover the interest payments to bondholders.

It was planned to organise four major events a year, an Indianapolis-style 500-mile race for USAC Championship cars, a 500-mile race for stock cars, a road racing event (for Formula One or Can-Am-type cars) and a national drag race meeting. Weekly drag race meetings, possibly professional sports car races and track-testing were envisaged, but amateur events were ruled out for 'the world's finest racing plant.' There was 'big thinking' all the way, the economic feasibility of the project costing out such items as expected attendance figures for the major promotions, television rights ($82,500 was anticipated for the first year, rising to $348,000 for the fifth), revenue from accessory firms and sponsors, etc.

Grand opening date was set for 6 September 1970, date of the California 500, a USAC National Championship race for Indianapolis-type machines. Indeed, the race closely resembled the Indy 500, 33 starters

Above: Reine Wisell leads Emerson Fittipaldi, both in Gold Leaf Team Lotus 72s, around Ontario in the 1971 Questor Grand Prix non-Championship race

qualifying to start the 200-lap event on the banked oval. Fastest qualifier in the four-lap times run was veteran Lloyd Ruby, the 42-year-old Texan averaging 177.567 mph in his Mongoose-Offenhauser. Slowest of all, at a 'mere' 169.101 mph, was the front-engined Mallard-Offenhauser of Jim Hurtubise. The race was watched by 180,223 fans—a record sports crowd in California—who groaned when Al Unser's seemingly invincible Colt-Ford succumbed to engine problems with 14 laps to go. Lee Roy Yarborough (Brabham BT32-Offenhauser) took control of the race, but he lost power and Art Pollard, whose Scorpion-Ford had started at the back of the grid, went ahead. With six laps to go Pollard had a puncture—he ran over the wreckage of A. J. Foyt's Coyote-Ford, which had crashed into a wall—and on the last lap was caught and passed by Jim McElreath's Coyote-Ford. McElreath, a 42-year-old Texan, became the first person to drive his car into Ontario Motor Speedway's Victory Circle (paved with bricks from Indianapolis); he averaged 160.606 mph for the 500 miles and collected $150,000.

On 28 March 1971, the next major promotion was run. This was the Questor Grand Prix, an event over two 102-mile heats on the combined road/track circuit for European Formula One and American Formula 5000 cars (Questor was a word dreamed up by a computer, being a holding company for the backers of the race). Although the European Grand Prix machinery triumphed (after a courageous effort by Mark Donohue's Penske-entered F5000 Lola T192-Chevrolet failed), victory did go to an American driver, Mario Andretti. Mario won both heats in his works Ferrari 312B-1/71, winning $39,400 and beating Jackie Stewart (Tyrrell 001-Ford) and Denny Hulme (McLaren M19A-Ford) on aggregate. Original plans called for the race to be given World Championship status in 1972 as the United States' *second* championship qualifier, but Questor withdrew their backing at the end of June when the Formula One Association greedily demanded a purse of $300,000 and refused to negotiate. No other sponsor could be found.

The second California 500, like the first, provided a surprise 'under-dog' winner. Run once more on Labor Day—Sunday, 5 September—it saw the favourites fail. Mark Donohue, whose Penske-entered McLaren M16A-Offenhauser had claimed pole position in qualifying with 185.004 mph, ran out of fuel, leaving the Unser brothers to fight for the lead. Bobby Unser's works Eagle-Offenhauser crashed into the wall, then Al Unser's Colt-Ford broke its gearbox. This left Joe Leonard to snatch victory in his Colt-Ford from Art Pollard's Brawner-Ford; Leonard also won $132,039 and scored sufficient points to move into the lead of the USAC Championship.

The 1972 race made history with Bobby Unser's works Eagle-Offenhauser setting a world closed-circuit speed record in qualifying: he averaged 201.374 mph, his best single lap being 201.965 mph. In the race A. J. Foyt's Coyote-Ford jumped into the lead, but succumbed to transmission failure. With both works McLarens and the three Parnellis failing, it was left to Mike Mosley (Eagle-Offenhauser) and Roger McCluskey (McLaren M16A-Offenhauser) to battle it out. Mosley's car suffered engine problems only five laps from the end, leaving McCluskey with a comfortable win; he finished with more than a lap's advantage over Mike Hiss (McLaren M16B-Offenhauser). McCluskey —who had won at Pocono earlier in the year— became the first man to win two 500-mile USAC races in a year.

But all was not going to plan at Ontario Motor Speedway. On 29 November 1972, the circuit was closed down. OMS Inc found it almost impossible to pay the $2 million annual rent (this represented almost 60% of the annual *gross* revenue) and defaulted on a payment. They hoped to propose to the OMS Corporation (ie, the bondholders) that the rental should be made on a percentage of profits rather than a set sum. In this way OMS Inc envisaged the circuit could continue to operate and bondholders would still get a return on their investment, although not the full 7½%. But Nuveen & Co of Chicago, the principle underwriter of the bonds, refused to send OMS Inc's proposal to the bondholders and the circuit had to be closed down. There were three avenues open: a new

company could be found to operate the circuit at the agreed terms; another proposal could be considered by the bondholders; or the circuit could be sold—at a mere fraction of its value.

On 9 January 1973, the track was apparently back in business. Western Racing Associates agreed to lease the Speedway from the City of Ontario for 12 months. The company, headed by Conrad Sprenger, the head of a local radio station, and financed by William Gillette, a member of the razor family, eventually backed out on the day the deal was due to be signed. In April another agreement was reached, this time with

racing driver/constructor Parnelli Jones and Indianapolis president Tony Hulman. The pair agreed to rent the Speedway for a year and had an option for a long-term lease. It was to transpire that at the end of 1973 Jones and Hulman bargained hard before they would sign the first five-year option on a 50-year agreement to manage the track. Originally, Jones' and Hulman's company—the Ontario Motor Speedway Operating Company—was scheduled to pay the bondholders $500,000 a year plus 50% of the profits to a maximum total of $950,000. Jones offered a yearly guarantee of $100,000 plus 50% of the profits with no ceiling. So as to avoid another track closure, a compromise was reached whereby OMSOC were to pay $150,000 the first year, $200,000 the second, $250,000 the third, $400,000 the fourth and $512,000 the fifth in addition to 50% of the profits. In fact, Nuveen & Co, representing the bondholders, gave the OMSOC a much better deal than that sought by the OMS Inc only twelve months before.

The 1973 California 500 saw a change of format with two 100-mile qualifying races a week prior to the major race. Winners were Wally Dallenbach (STP Eagle-Offenhauser) and Johnny Rutherford (works McLaren M16C-Offenhauser). By dint of driving more slowly than the pacemakers and thus making three fewer fuel stops, 36-year-old Dallenbach moved in front in the last 50 miles of the race to beat Mario Andretti's fast-closing Parnelli-Offenhauser by five seconds. In 1974 the race was moved to March and, despite the energy crisis, attracted 150,000 spectators. A. J. Foyt (Coyote-Ford) and Johnny Rutherford (McLaren M16C/D-Offenhauser) won the heats, while the 500-miler itself featured a titanic duel between the Unsers. Finally elder brother Bobby in his works Eagle-Offenhauser conquered Al by less than half-a-second to make it the closest finish in USAC history.

Patently the Ontario Motor Speedway project failed to live up to its founders' high expectations. However, it survives as an up-to-date, even luxurious, motor sporting facility hosting important motor races, motor cycle races and drag race meetings. It is highly improbable that it will ever become the world's top circuit, as had been intended.   MK

Above: as with most American Speedways, Ontario has its own drag-race strip. Here, a fueler 'burns out' prior to its actual run

SIMPLE ENGINEERING
and commercial courage

TO BE SUCCESSFUL in the motor industry it is not essential to make good cars, but it is absolutely vital to make good decisions. Opel make good cars now, and made some good ones at various times in the past, but in the course of their long history they also made some thoroughly bad ones. Notwithstanding the alternation of cadence and decadence decade by decade, they made themselves a tremendous reputation, and a rare kind of commercial invulnerability, not to mention a fortune; and the reason was that they always made the right decisions at the right times. As a result, they have been enormously successful, actually outselling Volkswagen on the German market in 1973 (with 406,000 regis-

the son of a locksmith in Rüsselsheim, then a small trading town. He embarked upon a career as a sewing-machine engineer, which occupied him for the rest of his life, from the foundation of the business in 1862. When he died in 1895, he left his widow Sophie the major interest in the firm, which she thereafter ruled firmly and shrewdly with the increasing help of her five sons. All the boys pursued technical studies, and were all distinguished racing cyclists, not merely from predilection but from the knowledge that the successes they gained would impress the customers for the bicycles that the firm was building in ever-increasing numbers since they began in 1887.

Right: one of the first Opel cars, based on the Lutzmann design. This single-cylinder, water-cooled 4½ hp car sold for 4000 Marks, complete with solid tyres

Above: the 10/18PS Phaeton Opel of 1908

Above right: the famous twin-cylinder Doctor's Coupé of 1908

trations against VW's 367,000), and, in 1975, were the second largest of all the divisions within the enormous General Motors organisation except for Chevrolet. In 1928, when they were still an independent family concern, Opel were Germany's largest car manufacturers and the world's biggest manufacturers of pedal cycles. Earlier still, they had been a big noise in sewing machines: by 1910, they had made and sold a million of them—and in 1911 they stopped. It was an early example of the Opel flair for acting decisively, if unexpectedly, for purely strategical business reasons.

The man who started the business, Adam Opel, was

Two years after Adam's death, the elder Opel brothers were appointed official observers of Germany's first motoring competition, a trial run from Berlin to Potsdam and back. The brothers felt that cars might be a new business that could reinforce the flagging work at Rüsselsheim, where the factory was suffering from the collapse of the bicycle market; and they took a special interest in the car that was judged to have performed best in the competition, a car built by another locksmith, Friedrich Lutzmann. After Benz and Daimler, Lutzmann was one of the pioneers of the motor vehicle in Germany, building his first car in

1893, and setting up a manufactory two years later under the official patronage of the Court of Anhalt. The Opel brothers enjoyed courtly patronage too, from Ernst Ludwig, the Grand Duke of Hesse, who was keen to advance the industrialisation of his duchy, and judged the Opels on their established record to be the best men to establish a motor industry in his domain. So, Carl and Wilhelm Opel went to see Lutzmann immediately after the Berlin event, and negotiated an agreement by which Lutzmann moved his machinery, workers and stock from Dessau to Rüsselsheim, where Lutzmann was put in charge of the new car department and set to develop suitable new models for Opel to make. By 1899, the first Opel cars were on sale—smaller, less ornate and more orthodox than the Dessau cars, and capable of about twelve mph under the spasmodic impulsion of a 4 hp 1½-litre single-cylinder engine, driving the rear wheels through a two-speed belt transmission. Starting these cars was pretty elemental: the driver reached down and seized the big flywheel, giving it a spin to start the engine.

How long it kept going was another matter. Cylinder bores were difficult to finish satisfactorily, and piston rings broke with depressing frequency. The Opels had to study entirely new skills and techniques, designing and building their own boring machines, experimenting with different ring materials and developing engines that ran faster and developed more power. They built a two-cylinder engine next, capable of driving a four-seater car at 27 mph, and experiments continued with such improvements as pneumatic tyres, an all-steel tubular chassis and stripped two-seater cars prepared for competition. With their cycling background, the Opels knew the value of racing successes, and it was an Opel that made the fastest time in one of the first hill-climbs held in Germany, near Heidelberg.

Despite their efforts, the Opels did not meet much initial success. Examining the products of their competitors at the Nuremberg Show early in 1900, they realised that the cars they were building to Lutzmann's designs were clumsy, backward, inelegant

Above: an Opel 2000 cc of 1912; this sporting four-cylinder car was manufactured in the year that Opel sales reached 10,000

and inefficient. It was the French who were making the real progress, with designs so radical that there was no hope of incorporating their features in the established Lutzmann-Opel designs. Lutzmann himself was proving a disappointment, devoting too much of his time to his own locksmithing inventions, and both production and sales from Rüsselsheim faltered. Eleven cars had been made in 1899, only 24 the following year, and the business was simply unprofitable. Mother Opel would not stand for that, and the car division was closed down, after all the components on hand had been assembled. Lutzmann was dismissed, never to return to the motor industry.

engine, after assembly by a skilled man and his assistant, was set up in the test-bench hall where it was motored over for at least ten hours, after which it was run for another ten under its own power. It was then dismantled, checked, reassembled and run for a further eight-hour cycle, under load for the final five hours. Similarly, gearboxes and axles were motored for five hours or more to ensure silent running, and after the complete chassis was assembled, it too was run on stands for several hours in all the gears. Only after a track test, under the burden of an extra-heavy test body, was the chassis passed for coachwork to be mounted, the painting of which alone occupied four

Below left: the 1911 6/16 hp Torpedo-Double Phaeton; this water-cooled four-cylinder car, with a capacity of 1540 cc, had a top speed of 37 mph

Below: the Prince Heinrich racers of 1910; the best of these 7.3-litre machines finished fourth

Two years later, after toying with motor-cycle manufacture, the Opel brothers pursued their faith in the car by entering into an agreement with Renault, giving them the exclusive representation of the make in Germany, but they soon discovered that the French company, still small, could not supply them with enough cars to justify the effort and investment involved. Accordingly, the brothers entered a further contract with Darracq, acquiring not only the agency for Germany and Austro-Hungary, but also the right to build their own bodies on Darracq chassis, and even to build cars to Darracq design. This was a well judged move: the Darracq was a good car, and was well received. Its single-cylinder 8 hp engine and a later 9 hp variant featured modern accoutrements such as shaft drive, with the chassis carrying a handsome four-seater body; and the car could be sold at 5000 marks, twice as much as the earlier Opel.

The Darracq business flourished, with the Opels continuing to import cars from France at the same time as introducing their own versions of Darracq designs, with more cylinders and different bodies. A two-cylinder 10/12 hp car was ready as early as the end of 1902, a four-cylinder car the following year, and two new versions of each in 1905. By that year, in which 358 cars were built, the Opels were well enough established for them to feel independent and they discontinued their co-operation with Darracq in 1906. Already they had become very active in sports and racing events, gaining more than 100 victories in 1905 —in which year, too, the firm was able to open a new car factory with its own power-generating plant. Much of the power was consumed in engine testing, for Opel devoted a lot of effort to ensuring the quality of their cars before releasing them from the factory. Each

weeks. Such cars were inevitably expensive, the dearest (the 6.9-litre 35/40 hp Opel) being priced at upwards of 17,000 marks. Equally inevitably, it was the small Darracq-inspired cars that enjoyed the greatest popular demand, especially a style-setting 8/14 hp two-cylinder 'doctor's coupé'.

Publicity was sought through further racing and sporting events. Special cars were built for the Kaiserpreis, one of the three major international events of 1907, and two of the team of three Opels survived to finish third and fourth. The race was won by Fiat, as were the other principal events of that year, but it was to Opel that Kaiser Wilhelm II personally presented his own trophy for the first German car to finish. This

Below and opposite page, top: two versions of the 1924 Opel *Laubfrosch;* these cars had 951 cc four-cylinder engines which produced 12 bhp at 2200 rpm

did a great deal of good to the Opel reputation, although the make suffered a setback in the 1908 French Grand Prix. In 1909, a relatively small four-cylinder Opel was entered for the rally-like Prince Henry (Prinz Heinrich) Trial, organised by the Kaiser's brother. Wilhelm Opel drove the winner, and other Opels were third, fifth, sixth, tenth and thirteenth. New cars were built to defend the title in 1910, low-built machines with overhead inlet valves in 7.3-litre engines said to develop more than 100 horsepower; the best of them finished fourth in a field that started more than 200 strong. Opel were doing well in every way—and then in 1911 the factory was destroyed by fire.

The Opels were nothing if not thorough: apparently they even had a master plan worked out in 1905 that set the rebuilding into motion forthwith, and by 1912 the new factory was open on the Golden Jubilee of the founding of the Adam Opel company. The Grand Duke did the honours again, with mother Sophie on his arm. In the following year she died, and the future of the firm was in the hands of the second generation, already mature industrialists whose sons were being trained for future participation. In that year, Opel began to build lorries, having already celebrated the delivery of their 10,000th car in 1912. The new factory had been designed to admit the most modern production techniques, and business once again flourished. The racing programme was not so successful: the cars built for the French Grand Prix of 1913 were failures, and the new one built for the 1914 event, with its engine modelled unashamedly on the twin-camshaft 16-valve four-cylinder Peugeots that had been so successful thanks to the design of Ernest Henry (and, it must be admitted, the inspiration of Hispano-Suiza's Marc Birkigt) could only finish in tenth place. Later that summer, the GP Opels were taken to Britain to race at Brooklands, but had to be abandoned there upon the outbreak of war. Years later, one of them was prominent at the track in the hands of a distinguished newcomer to the sport, Henry Segrave.

During the war, Opel naturally provided trucks and other vehicles for the army, and also built BMW aero engines, while completing in 1916 the prototype of their first six-cylinder car, which was intended for the post-war car market. Alas, the Opel master plan did not accurately forecast the immediate post-war situation: in December 1918, the French forces occupied Rüsselsheim, and ordered the destruction of tools, equipment and materials that could have been used to help rebuild the shattered nation's economy. The factory was declared within the demilitarised zone, which effectively meant that its supplies of raw materials and finance were restricted. Thugs terrorised the workers, the communists caused further upheavals and the antiquated cars that were all that could be put into production held very little attraction for the market, which had been reduced to a chaotic state by the runaway inflation of the currency.

Surprisingly, the currency of the Opel name was maintained by racing. The firm had completed a test track near the factory at the end of the war, a banked

concrete oval 1½ kilometres long. It was the only private testing track operated by any German car manufacturer, and it doubled as an excellent racing circuit. Frequent race meetings were held there, and even when Opel cars and drivers did not feature among the winners, the name was still advertised, because the place was known as the Opelbahn. Nor were Opel's racing activities confined to their own district: their leading driver Carl Jörns, who had joined them in the Darracq days, achieved some spectacular successes in an enormous racing two-seater built in 1913. This car had a 12-litre engine, built in Henry style, and was said to develop 260 horsepower, but distinguished by the location of the

Below: the 1913 racing Opel, which had a four-valves-per-cylinder, four-cylinder engine of no less than 12 litres. Power output was 260 bhp at 2900 and the car cost between 85 and 90 thousand Marks to develop

valve springs above the rockers so they projected above the engine and into the cooling air through holes in the bonnet—a valve-spring arrangement derived from a prototype Opel aero engine of 1911. In 1923, this car was timed at 206 kmh on the sands of Fanö, a Danish island where Malcolm Campbell had the day before just exceeded the existing land-speed record with 219.3 kmh.

The Opel brothers were by now more interested in production records than speed records. In the beginning of the decade they had set themselves to study the American methods pioneered by Olds, Leland, and Ford; and they were soon convinced that the profitable course for Opel would be to transform the Rüsselsheim plant with modern assembly lines for the quantity production of a low-cost car. While the national economic crisis reached its peak in 1923, with

Below: the Olympia Rekord 1.5-litre of 1958; This car was also available as a 1.7-litre

Bottom left: a 90 hp Opel, produced between 1959 and 1963

Bottom right: the 1963 Opel Rekord four-door

survive the maltreatment of the meanest French peasant and the roughest French roads, to give practical and economical transport to people who could afford nothing better and find nothing cheaper that was much good. This was what the Opels wanted, and this was what they made—almost a carbon copy, except for a magneto and 12V electrical system instead of a distributor and six volts, for minute differences in track and wheelbase, and for a slightly larger cylinder-bore dimension. Indeed, there was only one other significant difference: instead of being painted yellow, it was normally painted green, and so the Opel version too acquired a nickname, the *Laubfrosch* or Tree Frog.

The little green beasty was a tremendous success soon after it was put on the market in the spring of 1924. Stability was returning to the German economy, more quickly after the establishment of the Reichsmark in the August, and the miniature boom in the car business that then developed was ripe for exploitation more effectively by Opel than by any other domestic manufacturer. The car was progressively modified—if only to quieten the anger of Citroën, who had been prompted to take Opel to court for their candid plagiarism of the French design. Longer chassis, bigger engines, more capacious bodies, all followed in due turn, even six-cylinder cars; and as things grew progressively better, a six-litre straight-eight known as the Regent was introduced in 1929. Two years earlier, sales of the Tree Frog alone amounted to 39,000, and Opel had had the sense to build up a widespread service organisation throughout Germany. They were the first in the land to guarantee repairs at fixed prices, and their commercial acumen was rewarded with a 37.5% share of the German car output in 1928, by which time they had 8000 employees building 250 cars a day.

There were other statistics of even greater importance, however, for while their production was 37.5% of all German made cars, their sales were 44% of them—but only 26% of all the cars bought in Germany. The impact of the American industry on the German market had been far greater than expected. German cars had for obvious reasons fallen behind in technical progress, while the new exchange rate of the dollar to the mark made the prices of the American imports very favourable. Moreover, the tariff policies then current allowed American cars into Germany with only token payments of duty. It followed that the cars many Germans bought were American, and that they acquired a taste for them which prompted several of the few surviving German manufacturers (there were 65 in 1924, only 23 by 1928) to produce cars in the American idiom. Adler for instance built a virtual

the declaration of a state of emergency and the issue of a new currency, the Opels ripped out the old-fashioned countershafting of their factory, installed self-powered machines, scrapped all previous production models and insisted on a completely new start on everything in the drawing office. The only remaining question, and one that had to be answered quickly and correctly if the firm were not to collapse, was what car they should make.

Once again, the Opels found their inspiration in Paris. There, in 1919, Europe's first assembly line for mass production had been inaugurated by André Citroën, who in 1922 began building there a small car known as the Type C or 5 CV with a body style that earned it the connotation *Trèfle* or Cloverleaf—although the popular nickname was *Citron* or lemon, because it was usually painted yellow. It was a splendidly simple little four-cylinder motorcar, designed to

Chrysler, Stöewer a pseudo-Gardner, and when Opel were tempted to go and do likewise they were guided by their appreciation of quality to emulate the best of American practice, which was why the new cars marketed in 1927 resembled the current Packard. Even such stratagems as this, however, were not enough to protect the German manufacturers against the Americans. The big powers such as Ford and General Motors not only exported complete cars but also set up local assembly plants where cars could be put together from imported parts even more cheaply. GM had just such a factory in Berlin, but then transferred their attentions to England where, after failing to make the Austin Motor Company their own property, they bought the little Vauxhall company for a trifling $2\frac{1}{2}$ million dollars. The Opel family judged this to be of such significance that they made a proposition to GM the following year.

'The General' was in no hurry, and took time to act. Some of the senior GM administrators wanted to expand the Berlin factory into a manufacturing operation, while the President (Alfred P. Sloan, the visionary who made General Motors the magnificent giant it became during his office) favoured an affiliation with an existing German maker. Sloan and two aides called on Opel during a European trip late in 1928, and he was so impressed by what he saw that he promptly negotiated an option for GM to buy Opel. A team of investigators followed him, reporting favourably: 'The buildings were well designed, 70% of the machinery had been purchased during the past four years, and had been well selected. The plant was flexible and readily adaptable to new models. A good supply of high-class labour was available.'

The die was cast, and in January 1929, in preparation

Below left: the Opel Kapitän of 1962. This car had a 2.6-litre engine

Below right: this 125 bhp 2.8-litre Admiral was in production between 1964 and 1969

Bottom: the four-door Kadett, which was available with this body style from 1973 onwards

for the sale, the Opel family company was transformed into a joint stock company under the name that endures to this day, Adam Opel AG. In March 1929, GM took a substantial share of the stock, and in two subsequent transfers it bought the remainder, becoming the sole owner in October 1931, at a total cost of 66,724,000 dollars. It was not the beginning of the end, but it was the end of the beginning.

It was the end of a lot of things—of the bicycle business and of all the rallying and racing and general rocketing about, for instance. Some of the rocketing had been literal, not merely figurative: the exploits of the rocket-propelled Opel experimental speedsters of 1927 and 1928 still capture the imagination of enthusiasts and Opel's own publicists to this day. It was, in fact, a fairly casual affair, sparked off by a letter to Fritz von Opel by an Austrian author, lecturer and rocket enthusiast named Max Valier. He thought that the young von Opel (son of Wilhelm Opel who, with Carl and Heinrich, had been given aristocratic status by the Grand Duke, allowing them to use the name von Opel) might provide the money to support his proposed programme of rocket research, which was aimed at the ultimate development of rockets for flights into space. The two men met late in 1927 and, while Valier noted that young Fritz was interested in aviation, the latter realised that the demonstration of a rocket-powered car would be an inexpensive and very effective publicity stunt. He accordingly rushed Valier into the preparation of a rocket-propelled car, without embarking on any basic research in rocketry; so ready-made solid-propellant rockets were acquired from the specialist Sander, who made them for marine signalling and line-throwing. After experiments in secret with a hastily converted passenger-car chassis, the first special Opel rocket car, nicknamed *Rak* (for Rakete or rocket), was demonstrated before the press in April 1928. Although it did not go as fast as intended (only seven

of the twelve high-thrust rockets ignited properly), the smoke and noise of the 65 mph demonstration earned Opel tremendous newspaper publicity. This encouraged Opel to make a completely new car, the Opel *Rak II*, with an ultra-low chassis and a bullet-shaped body, sprouting two dozen rockets at the back and very large negative-incidence wings on each side to provide aerodynamic downthrust to ensure that the car remained on the ground and steerable. The angle of incidence of these wings could be adjusted by the driver, but when the time came, Fritz von Opel was too

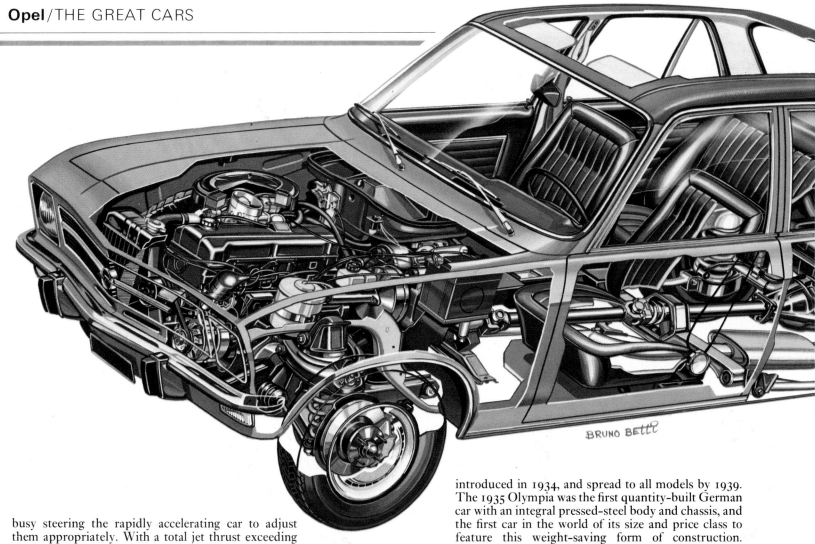

BRUNO BELLI

introduced in 1934, and spread to all models by 1939. The 1935 Olympia was the first quantity-built German car with an integral pressed-steel body and chassis, and the first car in the world of its size and price class to feature this weight-saving form of construction. The engine had an intriguing crankshaft: at a time when most four-throw cranks had three main bearings and some only two, while no mass-producer would

busy steering the rapidly accelerating car to adjust them appropriately. With a total jet thrust exceeding 13,000 lb, the car reached 142 mph while covering two kilometres of the Avus track, and the nose of the car started to lift!

To say that von Opel's aim was disturbed would be to confirm what Valier had felt for some time. The two men had entirely different objects, and eventually Valier went his own way. Fritz von Opel persevered with some unmanned rocket vehicles running on rails, and finally built his dream machine, a rocket-propelled aeroplane. After some false starts it made a clean take-off in September 1929, with the press looking on, but at an altitude of about 100 ft something went wrong and the aircraft made a heavy landing that was tantamount to a crash. The Opel rocket adventures were finished.

The General Motors adventure was already under way, under the aegis of the former Oldsmobile manager, I. J. Reuter, as Managing Director. While the world reeled in the great depression of 1930, his American and German engineers worked together on a new simplified range for 1931. It was a well planned, simple and thoroughly integrated range, employing many common parts, and based on a one-litre four-cylinder car and a 1.8-litre six that was like a miniature Cadillac. Alfred Sloan attracted some derision when he forecast eventual Opel production of 150,000 vehicles a year; the 1932 figure was only 20,982 cars and trucks, but within another seven years the annual output was within 6% of Sloan's prediction. Opels were marketed abroad as well as in Germany, the 1074 cc Kadett of 1937–1939 selling in England for a mere £135. Larger cars were successful, too, up to the 3.6-litre six-cylinder Admiral. The GM range of cars prior to the outbreak of World War II were cheap, effective, simple and by no means devoid of technical innovation. Independent front suspension of Dubonnet type was

Above: the sporty Opel Manta coupé, announced in 1970; power units for these cars were initially of 1.6 or 1.9 litres, although a subsequent 1.2-litre version was announced

dream of providing five, Opel did even better with four. In their engine, the place of the centre main bearing was taken by a bobweight that relieved the crankshaft of bending stresses. Stylistically, too, the Olympia was a pacemaker, with headlamps faired into the bonnet, valanced wings, enclosed spare wheel, and an alternative body style to the two-door saloon which was called a Cabriolet but was in fact less elegant, a simple saloon-type structure in which the steel roof panel was replaced by a fabric top that could be furled to leave the doors and window frames in position. As for the six-cylinder Kapitän of 1938, it not only had a unitary hull construction but also parallel-wishbone

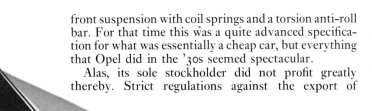

front suspension with coil springs and a torsion anti-roll bar. For that time this was a quite advanced specification for what was essentially a cheap car, but everything that Opel did in the '30s seemed spectacular.

Alas, its sole stockholder did not profit greatly thereby. Strict regulations against the export of

Left: announced shortly after the Manta was its saloon sister, the Ascona; engines available were the same as for the Manta

currency from Germany kept the Opel profits from reaching General Motors, who accordingly ploughed them back into the company. It was good for Opel but not entirely welcomed by the Nazi government, which did not like foreign domination of domestic industry. In 1940, an Opel official complained that more than 240 government departments were interfering with the company's affairs, and said that a single export sale required 54 documents to be completed. In June of that year, the whole situation became out of hand: GM declined the government's invitation to produce munitions in the Opel plant and, as it were, bit the bullet. They resigned from any and all responsibility for Opel activities, acknowledging 'with some regret that Mr Hitler is the boss of our German factory'. Car production at Rüsselsheim came to a halt in October

Above: the 2100 cc diesel Opel Rekord of 1972. This model shared the same body shell as the glamorous Commodore

after the production of 1,300,585 vehicles.

It did not do a great deal thereafter, not being considered trustworthy enough for major munitions assignments in view of its foreign associations. In any case, the Opel factories, both at Rüsselsheim and Brandenburg, were given a thorough going-over by the allied air forces, and by the beginning of 1945 there was very little left. The Russians seized the remains of the Berlin plant and transported it, lock, stock and barrel, to the Ural mountains—along with all the tools and drawings for the Kadett, which was put into production as the Moskvich 400. Not until December 1947 were GM allowed to resume car production at

Rüsselsheim, which they did with an updated version of the Olympia, but even then they were not allowed control of the company, and when in 1948 the possibility arose they were not at all sure that they wanted to take it. Finally, GM resumed management control of Opel in November 1948, and by 1953 output rose above 100,000 vehicles for the first time since the war.

They were not very prepossessing vehicles. Neither was the Moskvich, which retained its Opel characteristics until 1959, by which time Opel themselves were preparing to introduce a new Kadett. It eventually appeared in 1962, built in a new factory at Bochum. The next year, the Olympia became the Rekord, and alternative engine sizes were later offered, eventually with overhead-camshaft cylinder heads. Things gradually grew better, a notable technical step being the introduction of the surprisingly roadworthy Diplomat in 1965: handling the output of its 5.4-litre Chevrolet V8 engine was a well executed version of the de Dion rear axle, serving notice that the company's new engineers were intent on producing cars of much better road manners than had characterised their previous spongy lurchers. By 1969, a sporting image even became apparent, as the company began actively to support rallies. They even brought out what was called a GT coupé, in fact a beautifully streamlined little two-seater based on Kadett mechanical elements but enlivened by an optional 1.9-litre overhead-camshaft engine, checked by front disc brakes, and kept clean with the aid of retractable headlamps. In its faster version, this car could do 115 mph, handled impressively, and was extraordinarily stable in strong cross winds, even when running at very high speeds. The following year, 1970, saw the introduction of a new high-performance six-cylinder car, the Commodore, with fuel injection as an option.

A year later still came one of the most significant models produced in the most recent years, the Manta. This was a sporting coupé that was seen as Opel's answer to the Anglo-German Ford Capri, a car that was not only strikingly beautiful in its styling, but also blessed with impressive manners in everything from steering and roadholding to the adjustment of the elegant and comfortable seats. In time, it was given every imaginable treatment: there was an economy version, a luxury version, one with fuel injection, another with turbocharging. This last was not very satisfactory, prompting the British division of GM to commission a special turbocharging installation developed in England by Broadspeed. It appeared in 1974, but a much more important car based on the Manta platform was announced in 1971, only a fortnight after the Manta itself. This was the Ascona saloon, an outwardly ordinary family car that soon proved unexpectedly adept in international rallying.

Was the old competition enthusiasm of the Opel family showing through again? Not really: 'the General' was officially not interested in such chance-ridden and irrelevant activities. What had happened was the coalescence in Germany of a really gifted and enthusiastic design team, featuring Chuck Chapman as chief engineer, Chuck Jordan as chief stylist and Karl Brumm as chassis designer. Their next work, a completely new Kadett, proved at least as extraordinary in its combination of competence and simplicity as anything they or anybody else other than Fiat had ever produced. Only now was it emerging as the basis for a whole new generation of GM cars to be built in large numbers in countries all over the world. For the first time, a single basic design would satisfy all markets, an economical and compact car: once again, Opel did the right thing at the right time. LJKS

MANTA

The Opel Manta series of cars was introduced by the Rüsselheim company in 1971, and it was hailed as a worthy competitor to the similar-concept coupé car produced in Cologne and Dagenham: the Capri.

The Manta, then available in 1.6 and 1.9-litre forms, quickly earned a reputation for being a very nimble car: a combination of fat tyres, well sorted suspension and rack-and-pinion steering saw to that.

As time went on, various other Manta versions were announced, cheaper models with less trim, dearer models with more trim, fuel-injected models with that extra hint of power and, of course, the turbocharged derivatives that gave the Manta all the speed its chassis could reasonably take.

However, away from forced induction, the models available in early 1975 were the 1.6 DL, the 1.9 SR and the 1.9 Berlinetta. The 1.6 has a top speed of 101 mph, accelerates to 60 mph from standstill in 12.5 seconds and consumes fuel at the rate of 26 mpg, while the 1.9-litre versions have a top speed of 105 mph, accelerate from 0–60 mph in 11.4 seconds and cover 25 miles per gallon of fuel. A four-speed manual gearbox is standard, although a General Motors three-speed automatic unit can be specified.

ENGINE Front-mounted, water-cooled straight-four. 85 mm (3.34 in) bore × 69.8 mm (2.75 in) stroke = 1584 cc (96.7 cu in) (1.6), or 93 mm (3.66 in) bore × 69.8 mm (2.75 in) stroke = 1897 cc (115.8 cu in) (1.9) Maximum power (DIN) 80 bhp at 5200 rpm (1.6), or 90 bhp at 5100 rpm; maximum torque (DIN) 95 lb ft at 4200 rpm (1.6), or 108 lb ft at 2800 rpm. Cast-iron cylinder block and head. Compression ratio 9:1 (1.6), or 9.5:1 (1.9). 5 main bearings. 2 valves per cylinder operated, via pushrods and rockers, by a single side camshaft. 1 Solex 35 PDSI downdraught twin-choke carburettor.

TRANSMISSION Single-dry-plate clutch and four-speed manual gearbox, or torque converter and three-speed automatic gearbox. Ratios for manual 1.6 (1.9 version in brackets where differing). 1st 3.52 (3.42), 2nd 2.15, 3rd 1.36, 4th 1, rev 3.317:1. Ratios for automatic 1st 2.400, 2nd 1.480, 3rd 1, rev 1.920:1. Hypoid-bevel final drive. Ratio 3.67 manual, or 3.440 automatic.

CHASSIS Integral.

SUSPENSION Front—independent by wishbones, coil springs, an anti-roll bar and telescopic dampers. Rear—non independent by a rigid axle, coil springs, radius arms, a torque tube, Panhard rod and telescopic dampers.

STEERING Rack and pinion. Turns from lock to lock 3.

BRAKES Front discs, rear drums, servo assisted.

WHEELS 5.5 in × 13 pressed steel or light alloy.

TYRES 185/70 SR × 13.

DIMENSIONS AND WEIGHT Wheelbase 95¾ in; track—front 52.40 in, rear—51.97 in; length 169.98 in; width 64.02 in; height 52.95 in; ground clearance 4.72 in; dry weight 2100 lb; turning circle between walls 33.4 ft; fuel capacity 9.9 gals.

BODY Four to five-seater, two-door coupé.

PERFORMANCE Maximum speed 101 mph (1.6), or 105 mph (1.9). Acceleration 0–60 mph 12.5 secs (1.6), or 11.4 secs (1.9). Fuel consumption 26 mpg (1.6), or 25 mpg (1.9).

COMMODORE GS/E COUPE

The top of the Opel range in Great Britain is the Commodore GS/E coupé, priced, in early 1975, at almost £4500.

The power unit for the big five-seater coupé is a fuel-injected, 2.8-litre six-cylinder engine that produces 160 bhp at 5400 rpm and 168 lb ft torque at 4200 rpm. Such power gives the car a top speed of 121 mph and accelerates it to 60 mph in 10.4 secs when in the second of its three automatic-gearbox ratios. The fuel consumption for this 2900 lb car works out at 19 mpg overall.

Suspension at the front is by unequal-length wishbones, an anti-roll bar, coil springs and telescopic dampers, while the rear is non independent by a live axle with four links, a Panhard rod, an anti-roll bar, coil springs and telescopic dampers. Combined with a nice power-assisted steering system and fat 195-section tyres, the Commodore coupé has roadholding and handling usually set aside for smaller more nimble looking cars. Braking is taken care of by dual-circuit discs all round.

One of the main features of the car is the amount of fittings one gets in the standard price. They include a limited-slip differential, automatic transmission (although a manual unit is available at no extra cost), a wiper system for the headlamps, a laminated windscreen with a built-in radio aerial, a dashboard-mounted boot-release and a sunshine roof.

ENGINE Front-mounted, water-cooled straight-six. 92 mm (3.62 in) bore × 69.8 mm (2.75 in) stroke = 2784 cc (170 cu in). Maximum power (DIN) 160 bhp at 5400 rpm; maximum torque (DIN) 168 lb ft at 4200 rpm. Cast-iron cylinder block and head. Compression ratio 9.5:1. 7 main bearings. 2 valves per cylinder operated by an overhead camshaft. Bosch mechanically operated fuel injection.

TRANSMISSION Torque converter and GM automatic gearbox. Maximum ratio of converter at stall 2:1. Ratios 2.40, 2nd 1.48, 3rd 1, rev 1.92:1. Hypoid-bevel final drive with a limited-slip differential. Ratio 3.45:1.

CHASSIS Integral.

SUSPENSION Front—independent by unequal-length wishbones, an anti-roll bar, coil springs and telescopic dampers. Rear—non independent by a live axle with four links, a Panhard rod, an anti-roll bar and telescopic dampers.

STEERING ZF power-assisted ball and nut. Turns from lock to lock 4.5.

BRAKES Servo-assisted discs all round, with dual circuit.

WHEELS 6 in × 14 pressed steel.

TYRES 195HR 70 × 14.

DIMENSIONS AND WEIGHT Wheelbase 105 in; track—front 57.09 in, rear 55.6 in; length 181.38 in; width 68.03 in; height 55.31 in; ground clearance 6.02 in; dry weight 2712 lb; turning circle between walls 34 ft; fuel tank capacity 15.4 gals.

BODY Five-seater, two-door coupé.

PERFORMANCE Maximum speed 120 mph. Acceleration 0–60 mph 10.4 secs. Fuel consumption 19 mpg.

A MASERATI WITHOUT THE NAME

In 1938, the Maserati brothers sold out to the Orsi's, but in 1947 they re-emerged to build OSCAs. These never, however, captured the 'Maserati' flavour

Above left: Ernesto Maserati at the wheel of the first OSCA, the 1948 1100 cc MT 4

Above: Serafini guides the 1342 cc MT 4 OSCA on its way in the 1949 Circuito del Garda

Left: the first OSCA, seen this time with bodywork in place

Right above: Ernesto Maserati again. This time he stands next to the company's 1952 Formula Two contender

Right below: the 60° V12 engine as used in the 1951 Grand Prix car, seen *opposite page, bottom*

THE STORY OF OSCA begins over half a century before the birth of the marque. An Italian engine driver's six sons, the Maserati brothers, became passionately involved with motor cars. They were Carlo, Bindo, Alfieri, Mario, Ettore and Ernesto. Carlo, the eldest, was chief test driver for Fiat before joining Bianchi, for whom he also raced. He died at the age of 30, by that time running the Junior car firm and being involved with the design and construction of aero engines.

Mario preferred a paintbrush to a spanner and became an artist. Alfieri began to race, while Bindo became test driver for Isotta Fraschini. After World War I, Officine Alfieri Maserati, which had started as a repair shop some years before, began to grow. Alfieri, Bindo and Ettore (who had been involved with Alfieri in the construction of a racing car in Argentina before the war) were joined by the youngest brother Ernesto (a wartime pilot) and the four designed, built and prepared racing cars. For two years they developed Isotta Fraschini machinery, then Diattos and finally, in 1926, cars which bore their own name, Maseratis.

The brothers lived a hand-to-mouth existence. They were far happier building the cars in the little factory at Bologna than attending to the administration. In 1932 they suffered their first major setback when their company's founder and head, Alfieri Maserati, died; he had never fully recovered from an operation following a crash in the Targa Florio some years earlier. Bindo, Ettore and Ernesto decided to carry on, the last-named now head of the firm which had built and sold some highly successful racing cars. The next crisis came in 1937. Sales dropped as the brothers' cars were not as competitive as before, one of the reasons being the domination of the German Mercedes-Benz and Auto Union teams in Grands

Right: Luigi Fagioli gets an enthusiastic send-off in his 1100 cc car on the 1950 Mille Miglia

Above: the 1500 cc OSCA record car, run at Utah in 1955

Prix. In financial difficulties, they sold out to two wealthy industrialists from Modena, Adolfo Orsi and his son Omer. The Maseratis were retained on a 10-year contract and supervised the design and development of new models. In the early post-war years Maserati once more became one of the most prolific racing car manufacturers.

In 1947, their contract to the Orsis expired, Bino, Ettore and Ernesto Maserati left Modena to return to Bologna where, with the minimum of capital, they established a new company in a portion of their old, pre-1937 factory. It was known as OSCA (Officine Specializzate Costruzioni Automobili Fratelli Maserati); the brothers had been forbidden to use their own name by the Orsis. The intention was to revive the pre-Orsi days at Maserati by designing and building racing cars for the private owner. The three brothers—who did not drink, smoke or visit the theatre or cinema, such was their devotion to motor racing—started work with one lathe, one vertical drill, one shaper and one milling machine. The drawing office was Ernesto's bedroom. Ernesto was officially the development engineer, Ettore the tooling-up engineer and Bindo the plant manager.

In 1948 their first machine appeared, an 1100 cc sports car which was also raced with success in Formula Two. In Naples, Luigi Villoresi drove the car in Formula Two guise to victory ahead of such notable opposition as Raymond Sommer (Ferrari) and Alberto Ascari (Maserati). Onlookers marvelled at the high standard of workmanship of the OSCA. The engine was a square (equal bore and stroke) four cylinder with a capacity of 1089 cc. Its specification included a chain-driven single overhead camshaft, a light alloy cylinder head and a fully-balanced five-bearing crankshaft. Two horizontal Weber carburettors were employed and a power output of 80 bhp at 6000 rpm quoted. The chassis frame comprised basically two large-diameter tubes braced by cross-members, a ladder-type arrangement that was the hallmark of the Maserati brothers. Front suspension was by unequal length wishbones,

torsion bars and dampers, while at the rear was found a rigid axle in a light alloy casing sprung by half-elliptics.

The same basic sports car design remained in production for years to come, with engines ranging in size from 750 cc to 1½ litres becoming available. But the Maseratis yearned to re-enter Grand Prix racing and in 1951 the Siamese prince B. Bira commissioned them to design and build a 4½-litre V12 engine to install in his Maserati 4CLT/48 chassis. By this time the 1½-litre supercharged engine of the Maserati was outclassed in Formula One and Bira hoped a more powerful engine—330 bhp at 7000 rpm was quoted for the 60-degree V12 engine of 78 mm by 78 mm, 4472 cc—would once more make the car competitive.

The OSCA's début was at Goodwood on Easter Monday. 'Bira' won the Richmond Trophy Formula One race and finished third in the Chichester Cup, also breaking the course lap record at 90.35 mph. At San Remo the radiator was damaged in a collision and after finishing fourth at Bordeaux Bira was third in his heat at Silverstone; the final was curtailed owing to a downpour. At the Whitsun Goodwood meeting the OSCA won its heat, but in the final dropped out with

Top left: Colin Davis with an OSCA Junior in the 1960 Pescara GP

Top right: Colin Davis again, this time with the 1958 750 cc Le Mans car

Above: a rare example of a four-cylinder 1500 cc OSCA, now in the San Martino museum

oil pump failure after raising the lap record to 92.12 mph.

A ski-ing accident prevented Bira from racing again until October, but a complete Formula One OSCA was on the grid for the Italian Grand Prix at Monza in September. Its chassis was of the familiar tubular ladder-frame construction, while the suspension was by unequal length wishbones plus coil springs and an anti-roll bar at the front and by means of a de Dion tube located laterally by a Panhard rod at the rear. Driven by Franco Rol, it finished ninth and last, lapped 13 times by Ascari's winning Ferrari. The OSCA was plainly overweight and under-powered and only appeared again after conversion to a sports car.

Following the success of converted sports cars in Formula Two, new six-cylinder 2-litre single-seaters appeared in 1952 and 1953 driven by Elie Bayol and Louis Chiron. The engine, a 1987 cc unit with a bore and stroke of 76 mm by 73 mm, featured twin overhead camshafts and developed 160 bhp at 6500 rpm. Chiron won at Aix-les-Bains and finished second at Syracuse and Sables d'Olonne, while Bayol was second at Albi. At this time the Maseratis collaborated with the French Gordini firm; Gordini at one time considered

Above: a 1960 1000 cc car seen at Vallelunga

Above right: the 2000 cc OSCA sports car of 1960; this car's four-cylinder engine featured a desmodromic valve system

Right: the Artom collection now has possession of this four-cylinder 1500 cc car

building a Formula One car using the $4\frac{1}{2}$-litre V12 engine, while it was no coincidence that both OSCA's and Gordini's new Formula Two engines were originally going to be V8s but instead proved to be 'sixes'.

OSCA's chief successes came in sports car racing, especially in the rugged Italian road races such as the Mille Miglia and Targa Florio. From the original 1089 cc engine were evolved the 1342 cc (75 mm by 76 mm) model and the 1453 cc (78 mm by 76 mm) version. It was in a $1\frac{1}{2}$-litre OSCA, owned by the American Briggs Cunningham, that Stirling Moss and Bill Lloyd took a sensational, if brakeless, victory in the 1954 Sebring 12-hours in Florida. Their diminutive machine vanquished cars with many times its engine capacity. This success resulted in a host of enquiries from the United States and a new factory was opened in 1955 four miles south-east of Bologna at San Lazzaro di Savena.

By 1958 production had reached between 20 and 30 cars a year, all cars being handbuilt by the workforce of 40. One of the few items supplied by an outside concern was the bodywork. Three models were available, all sports cars, for the 750, 1100 and 1500 cc sports car classes. A development of the original engine

of 10 years before, the Tipo 187 748 cc unit developed 70 bhp; the Tipo 273 1092 cc engine gave 95 bhp and the Tipo 372 1491 cc over 135 bhp. All three featured two twin-choke Weber carburettors which fed the mixture into hemispherical combustion chambers with central Marelli plugs and two valves per cylinder. The twin overhead camshafts were driven by gears and a short chain.

Above: the 1600 cc, 100 bhp OSCA GTS of 1962; various coach-builders made bodies for this car, including Zagato and Touring

1597

An experimental desmodromic valve 1490 cc engine was seen from time to time in sports car racing and the 1½-litre Formula Two of the late 1950s. It performed well, and reliably, but as there was no real power advantage gained in having mechanically rather than spring-closed valves the project was shelved. OSCA had, of course, to consider the service aspect—many of their customers were in the United States—and, of course, cost.

Towards the end of 1959 a new category opened the way for more OSCA sales. This was Formula Junior, a new single-seater class intended as a cheap introduction to motor racing for new drivers. Engines of 1 litre or 1100 cc had to be derived from production units. OSCA's answer was a front-engined machine of their usual ladder-frame construction. Front suspension was by unequal length wishbones and coil spring/damper units and a live axle was sprung by vertical coil springs at the rear. Power came from an OSCA-modified Fiat 1100 engine which developed a healthy 78 bhp at 7500 rpm. Works driver Colin Davies (a Briton who lived in Italy and the son of pre-war Bentley exponent and journalist S. C. H. Davis) found plenty of success in Italian races in 1960, winning a so-called World Championship for Formula Junior cars run by an Italian magazine. But the writing was on the wall. Rear-engined, independently-suspended British machinery quickly got a stranglehold in Formula Junior and by 1961 the OSCAs were also-rans on the race tracks.

OSCA produced a 2-litre sports car featuring a four-cylinder engine of 88 mm by 81.5 mm (1995 cc) which produced 175 bhp at 6500 rpm, but lack of funds prevented its proper development. In 1960 the 750 cc sports car had a reworked engine, the Tipo 187N; it had a shorter stroke (64 mm by 58 mm), a completely revised cylinder head and a power output raised to 75 bhp at 7700 rpm. A desmodromic-valve 1100 cc engine was also made available to United

States customers, while the 1½-litre engine found its way into Formula One cars designed and built by former OSCA customer Alessandro de Tomaso, an Argentinian living in Italy, but they lacked sufficient power. Work progressed on a completely new Formula One engine design under the direction of Fabio Taglioni, of Ducati motorcycle fame, but this V8 (rumoured to be air-cooled and with desmodromic valve gear) never saw the light of day and neither did OSCA's proposed spaceframe chassis (at last a rear-engined design).

Into the 1960s OSCA concentrated on the production of a series of Grand Touring cars. The reason for this step dates back to 1959 when Fiat asked to use the OSCA twin-cam sports car engine in their Farina-bodied 1200 model. Fiat built the engine in Turin, increasing the engine capacity to 1568 cc (80 mm by 78 mm) and detuning it to produce 100 bhp at 6000 rpm. In turn, the Maserati brothers used the Fiat-produced engine (in more potent form) in cars of their own featuring bodywork by such stylists as Touring, Fissore, Boneschi and Zagato, the last-named producing a sporting coupé. Some OSCAs—notably the Zagato-bodied GTS with a 140 bhp engine—were raced, but no noteworthy successes were recorded on any of the world's circuits.

In 1963 OSCA became part of the MV Agusta concern, a company specialising in the construction of helicopters. Its boss, Count Dominico Agusta, built and raced high-performance motor cycles as a hobby and there was speculation that with the acquisition of OSCA he might be tempted to challenge fellow Italian Enzo Ferrari by building a Grand Prix car. As it was to transpire, this was not the case. OSCA GT models continued to be built for some time, while the ageing Maserati brothers experimented with various projects, but eventually production ceased and OSCA became part of motoring history like so many others before them. MK

Above: Prince Bira's 4½-litre Grand Prix car of 1951; as can be seen, the car is finished in the splendid colours of the Siamese Prince

FIRST WITH THE FOUR STROKE

Nikolaus Otto died just as the motoring age was beginning, but his name is inseparable from the four-stroke cycle

IT IS USUAL TO CREDIT the German inventor Nikolaus August Otto with the invention of the internal-combustion engine as we know it, but Herr Otto was really only one link in a long chain that stretched back to the genteel drawing-room chemistry of the Georgian era and the discovery that certain gases in combination could cause a combustible mixture.

'There is a mode of using this apparatus (said Mrs B) which produces still more powerful effects. It consists in condensing in the reservoir, not oxygen alone, but a mixture of oxygen and hydrogen in the exact proportion in which they unite to produce water, and then kindling the jet formed by the mixed gases. The heat

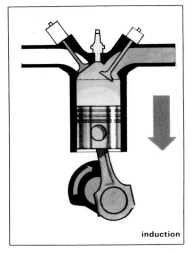 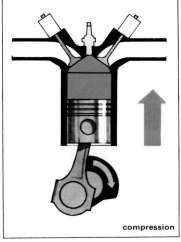 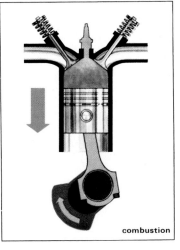 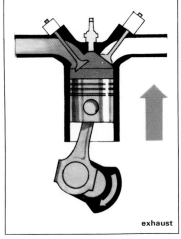

induction   compression   combustion   exhaust

disengaged by this combustion, without the help of any lamp, is probably the most intense known, and various results are said to have been obtained from it which exceed all expectation.'

'But why should we not try this experiment?' (asked Caroline).

'Because it is not exempt from danger; the combustion (notwithstanding various contrivances which have been resorted to with a view to prevent accident) being apt to penetrate into the inside of the vessel, and to produce a dangerous and violent explosion . . .'

However, even when those words were written, in an 1820s treatise, *Conversations on Chemistry*, there were inventors attempting to contain that 'dangerous and violent explosion' and turn its force into useful work. As early as 1791, John Barber had patented a crude gas turbine intended to employ 'inflammable air . . . for the purpose of procuring motion' while, three years later, Robert Street actually suggested using the upstroke of a piston in an upside-down cylinder to draw in a combustible gas produced from tar or turpentine, plus a flame that would explode it.

Then, in 1804, the Frenchman Phillipe Lebon d'Humberstein patented a double-acting two-stroke engine running on illuminating gas, with ignition by electricity. He was assassinated before he could turn his patent into reality, though.

In 1814, claimed the *Journal of the Franklin Institute*, an inventor had given the editor a model of an 'inflammable air' engine which appeared to work with considerable power, although the first internal-combustion unit to drive a road vehicle (if we discount the Swiss Isaac de Rivaz's crude powered cart of 1805, which could only travel the width of a room) was built in 1826 by the Londoner Samuel Brown, whose 40-litre 'gas and vacuum' carriage climbed Shooters Hill in Woolwich to the satisfaction of numerous spectators.

The first major progress in the concept of the internal-combustion engine came in 1854, when the

Above: there are four stages to the Otto or four-stroke cycle: induction, compression, combustion and exhaust. This means that there is only one power stroke for every two crankshaft revolutions. On the induction stroke, the piston is travelling downwards with the inlet valve open, thus drawing fuel and air into the cylinder; as the piston approaches the bottom of its stroke, the inlet valve closes and the mixture is then compressed by the piston's upward movement; near the top of the stroke, the mixture is ignited and combustion forces the piston downwards; at the bottom of the stroke, the exhaust valve opens, the waste products then being forced out to complete the cycle

Italian inventors Eugenio Barsanti and Felice Matteucci patented a two-stroke power unit in which the explosion took place beneath a free piston which imparted motion to a working piston attached to a rack rod which, as it rose and fell, turned a gear-wheel. In 1856, such an engine was installed in a Florence railway station, while in 1860 a company was formed to exploit the invention. Around this time, a 20 hp engine was supplied to the Escher Wyss company of Zurich, while a 4 hp version was later built for the Officine Bauer Elvetica di Milano. It seems that the Barsanti/Matteucci engine was also built under licence by Cockerill of Liège, but Barsanti died in Liège in 1864 while arranging the terms of this licence, and the invention was exploited only to a minimal extent.

Lenoir's non-compressing gas engine of the same period enjoyed a greater commercial success, and it was an 1860 press report of this machine that inspired Nikolaus August Otto, who was then 28 and working as a clerk in a Cologne shop, to attempt to develop an internal-combustion engine which could be used where steam power was impracticable.

Working with his brother, Wilhelm, Otto devised an internal-combustion engine working on liquid hydrocarbon fuel but, when he attempted to patent it, the Prussian Ministry of Commerce rejected the application on the grounds that the proposed engine was too similar to the Lenoir unit. Next, Otto conceived an improved version of the Barsanti and Matteucci engine; this, too, proved unpatentable.

However, now Nikolaus Otto met Eugen Langen, a well-to-do engineer from Cologne, and the two men built an engine in which the gas mixture was compressed *before* it entered the cylinder (surely the first crude attempt at supercharging) and ignited by a flame, while the working stroke of the engine was controlled by a flywheel. This was, however, still a crude free-piston engine, needing a great deal of headroom above the long rack rod which rose and fell vertically.

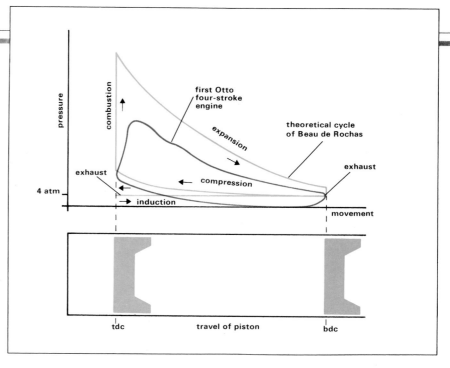

Langen's friend, Fritz Reuleaux, formerly professor of Mechanical Engineering at Zurich, now took over the Mechanical Engineering chair at the Berlin Institute for Trade, and in his new capacity gave the inventors all the help and encouragement he could. When Reuleaux was seconded to the Technical Committee for Trade, which dealt with all patent applications, it was virtually a foregone conclusion that an application from Otto and Langen to patent their power unit would be favourably considered. Sure enough, the patent was granted on 21 April 1866.

The following year, Otto and Langen entered their machine for the Paris World Exhibition, where the ubiquitous Reuleaux was a judge of the engineering exhibits; the Otto engine was awarded the Gold Medal for its superiority to the other gas engines on display. Although two attempts to build Lenoir engines in Germany had failed through lack of demand, Otto and Langen attempted commercial production of their power unit. Little success resulted until 1872, though, when the company was reorganised as the Gas-Motoren-Fabrik Deutz, with Gottlieb Daimler as factory manager in charge of production.

The same year, George B. Brayton, an Englishman resident in Boston, Massachussets patented a non-compressing power unit which operated on similar principles to the Ericcson hot-air engine. The *Scientific American* compared the two engines in an 1876 supplement: 'The Brayton machine is a fine piece of workmanship, and in its working is smooth and equable, resembling in all respects, externally, a well-proportioned steam-engine. The Langen & Otto engine, however, looks like any thing rather than it, and its action is widely different. When the charge is fired beneath the piston, the latter, with the rack attached, is shot upwards with great velocity, descending slowly while in connection with the shaft, giving to it a very irregular and uncomfortable appearance, causing a vague kind of fear that the whole piston and rod or rack might be projected from the cylinder. After a little watching of it, however, this feeling wears off, and as the sudden impulses given the piston are found to recur with perfect regularity, one begins to have confidence in it, and to believe that this, as well as the Brayton machine, is an ingenious and creditable piece of work.'

Although Daimler and Maybach had succeeded in raising their output to ninety engines a month, and some 2700 Otto & Langen engines were in use in Germany and England, it was obvious that there was little more that could be achieved with this noisy and inefficient power unit. Reuleaux sounded a warning: 'Otto must get on his hind legs and Daimler on his front legs'.

Above left: the man whose name was on the patent for the four-stroke-cycle—Nikolaus August Otto

Above: a graphical representation of the pressure changes that take place during the various stages of the Otto cycle

The great breakthrough that was needed, however, would come from neither man: personality clashes threatened to split the company, and Daimler recommended a new chief engineer, Franz Rings, who carried on research under Otto's personal direction. Rings abandoned the idea of developing the two-stroke free-piston engine any further, and instead turned to a concept that Otto had tried and abandoned in 1861–62, the four-stroke cycle.

On 9 May 1876, Rings drew up a four-stroke engine in his research diary, and Hermann Schumm, another Daimler protégé, began building prototypes, which were finished and tested by September/October the same year. The only weak point of the design was the ignition system, in which a slide valve exposed a flame to the combustion chamber, a complex system of non-return passages obviating blow-back.

Now, though, the personality clashes between Langen and Daimler became more unpleasant, resulting in Daimler's resignation in 1882.

Otto attempted to create a monopoly of the four-stroke cycle, thus forcing other experimenters to concentrate on the two-stroke or risk prosecution, but his plans for control of the industry were dashed. This was when his 1877 patent was overthrown after two years of litigation in 1886, on the grounds that an obscure French civil engineer named Alphonse Beau de Rochas, prematurely retired at the age of 45, had distributed 300 copies of a memorandum describing the four-stroke cycle to the Press in 1862, and had patented the concept.

Nikolaus Otto died in 1891, at the dawn of the motor age, although his company continued. They built a range of Bugatti-designed cars in 1907–11, and later entered the field of commercial vehicles and tractors, in which the Magirus-Deutz name was to become famous; Otto's son, Gustav, designed the Otto car which was produced in 1923–24 in Munich.

It was, however, the concept of the four-stroke cycle rather than its application to a motor vehicle that earned Nikolaus August Otto his place in automotive history—indeed, the four-stroke cycle is still alternatively referred to as the Otto cycle. And yes, there *was* an Otto cycle that you could ride, too. Built in the 1880s, the Otto Dicycle was a fiendish device in which the rider balanced precariously between two side-by-side wheels devoid of any steadying mechanism. BSA built the machine in Britain but, hardly surprisingly, it failed to enjoy any lasting success. DBW

THE TERM OVAL RACING has, over the years, become almost synonymous with stock-car racing, largely due to the immense popularity the latter has achieved in Europe over the past decade. In fact, there is not much in the way of oval racing apart from stock-car racing, not in the accepted sense of the word, anyway.

Stock-car racing, though, covers a multitude of cars and drivers in its own right. Some of them, like grass-track racers and bangers, might object to being described as stock cars but it is a loose definition and serves well to define any form of motor sport which takes place on a small oval track (usually) with a loose surface (usually) and in which metal-to-metal contact between the cars is not unknown, to say the least!

Today, oval racing in England is a highly sophisticated and well organised form of motor sport, and is one of the few motor sports, in fact, at which a reasonable number of drivers can actually make a living. Unlike Grand Prix racing, though, finance is not such a huge obstacle to a budding short-oval star wishing to make his name: he can start with as little as the price of an old MG Magnette rescued from a scrap yard. Furthermore, instead of paying an entrance fee, on most circuits he will get paid a little start money!

Oval racing has had many ups and downs of both a financial and a physical nature in the twenty odd years since it came to the United Kingdom, and has always been something of an enigma to those people who think of motor racing as being purely a pastime for well heeled young men. The most denigrated and despised of motor sports, it can also be wildly exciting and colourful, a heart-stopping spectacle of power and speed with every lap packed with action and danger. There are many who still refuse to regard it as anything but a game for noisy yobs of gypsy extraction, and it very, very rarely gets mentioned in the enthusiast motoring press unless it be to illustrate an unfavourable comparison or comment on a circuit driver's aggressive

SPEED IN THE STADIUM

There are various forms of oval racing, ranging from 'banger' to hot-rod, all taking place on dirt tracks

Below: author Andy Anderson with rodders Collard and Lee

Bottom: stock-car action

style. 'He should take up stock-car racing,' they say, both as a reflection on a driver's tactics and his manners.

It is interesting to consider how this attitude came into being, apart from the obvious observations that,

sport mushroomed as no other form of motor sport ever did. The bubble was shortly to burst, though, for the growth rate had been far too explosive. Attendances fell off rapidly in 1956 and by the end of that year, no more than a handful of promoters were still in business.

That first meeting was an interesting one. It was won by a Frenchman, D'Orgieux, from the Buffalo stock-car stadium in Paris, but he probably did not get as much attention from that huge crowd as the driver of car number 38, the remarkable lady driver Tanya Crouch. She came fourth that night, but regularly beat the men in her big Ford and was extremely popular, driving her car on the road to races in different parts of the country.

Those first two years must have been startling times. Promoters would sign drivers up to race only at their stadiums, and squabbles over signings inevitably broke out. The racing was rough, tough and dangerous, too, with few of the safety features that were later so rigidly enforced as fittings to race cars. There was much disagreement about the weight of cars that should be allowed, too. Some of the heavier cars weighed as much as two tons, and these were capable of making a nasty mess of the lighter models. This fact led to many violent post-race scenes in 1956, usually instigated by drivers of lighter (and, as a result of the race, shorter) cars who felt aggrieved at being bulldozed around by the heavyweights.

The cars were usually large American saloons that few people could have afforded to run on the road even

being cheap to compete in and having stadiums within large-city boundaries, oval racing became a motor sport for the working man, who possibly did not have his own car and could not afford a long day trip out of town to watch cars compete against each other. At the same time, the very nature of the sport is that cars get damaged. Obviously they are not replaced with new cars, so the second-hand-car trade, or that part of it which deals with cars on their last legs, comes into the picture, as do scrapyards, and this apparently seedy pairing does not naturally make for a form of motor sport with a high social standing.

Stock-car racing had a good enough start in this country, though. An Australian promoter called Digger Pugh was the first to bring it to England, after having watched it in both America and France. He held his first big event at New Cross stadium in south-east London in 1954, aided and abetted by racing driver turned broadcaster/journalist John Bolster. They drew between twenty-five and thirty-thousand people to that first event—far bigger crowds than attend meetings two decades later.

The instant success of the new form of motor sport brought a gleam to the eyes of many ambitious promoters, and the next two years saw much hectic activity. Almost forty tracks were opened, and the

Above: A Volkswagen Hot Rod complete with Mercedes grille

Above right: Hot Rod superstar Barry Lee stands by his trusty Ford Escort in his lamé Nomex suit. The air scoop on the back of Barry's car leads to the final drive, which gets very hot during a race

if they had been roadworthy. They were fast and powerful, and withstood the terrible pounding they were frequently subjected to. However, it was not long before the desire for lighter and even speedier cars led to people taking the bodies off them and substituting vestigial European saloon-car bodies. Frequently they would design new chassis for their cars, too, so that the only remaining part was the American engine.

Some promoters did not approve of the way the sport was going, feeling that such diversification could only lead to more expense in the long run. The situation was eventually to result in the setting up of different formulae, winding up with the position where there were many different classes.

It was, perhaps, in those early years that the sport was at its most glamorous, in a scruffy sort of way. The violence and destruction, the lurid antics of the big cars and the flamboyant attitudes and antics of the drivers—who often had colourful nicknames—did not prevent the attendances dropping off radically, though. The famous drivers were Aubrey Leighton, Johnny Brise, Doug Wardropper and Vic Ferriday, but there were many more of similar quality.

After a quiet year or so, stock-car racing started to pull itself together again in 1958 and 1959. The British Stock Car Drivers Association extended its influence, and many of the tracks were improved. By this time, the best ones were at Brafield, Manchester Belle Vue and Coventry, and several meetings were televised. Real diversification came in 1961, with a major split in the promotional set-up. One Les Eaton, after a disagreement with the existing promoters in the South, formed his own promotional organisation. This outfit came later to be known as Spedeworth, and outside America, in 1975, was the largest stock-car promoting company in the world. In the early sixties, Eaton ran meetings at Ipswich, Aldershot and Eastbourne, and several more tracks were opened in the next few years. While the BSCDA, the other body, had reached a stage of development with its cars, Eaton was to develop several separate classes based on the different ways drivers were already beginning to build their cars at the start of that second decade of stock-car racing. It was also Les Eaton who made his brand of stock-car racing truly international, taking teams of drivers to race on the Continent and eventually running meetings in South Africa over the British close season.

The emergence of the new formulae took place slowly over the years until in 1968 there were four formulae being run on the Spedeworth tracks and two with the British Stock Car Association (the word 'drivers' had been dropped from the title by this time).

First, were the Spedeworth Stock Cars. These were perfectly standard family saloon cars with a limit of 1800cc capacity. For reasons of their strength and durability, ninety per cent of stock cars seemed to be MG Magnettes. The interior furnishings were all ripped out for lightness, leaving usually just a seat, a steering wheel, pedals, an oil-pressure warning light, seat belts, and a petrol tank inside to keep the driver company. The petrol tank was located as near to the centre of the car as possible to minimise the chance of rupturing it in an accident. The car was strengthened with the use of large-section steel tubing which was installed right through the length of the car. Hefty bumpers were welded to the ends of this supplementary chassis and, apart from the addition of extra plates on the wheels to keep them from being torn off, that was a stock car. They seemed to keep going despite the most horrific crashes, and cars in the most amazing stages of delapidation frequently won!

Top: the public love to see shunts like this in stock-car racing, but the drivers rarely get hurt

Centre: to prove the point, a driver climbs through the window aperture (the cars' doors are welded up for safety) of his MG Magnette after it has expired and overturned

Left: Dave Taylor trying hard in his Ripspeed Mini Rod

Midget racing was also a regular feature of Spedeworth meetings. It was not new then, having been seen in England on the Speedway circuits before the war. Basically, a midget was a small, open-wheeled racing car with a water-cooled 1250cc maximum capacity engine, although a few cars with V8 power were seen. Midgets were fast and bore a certain resemblance to circuit racing cars, but they were never very popular, probably because they did not crash much, and crashes are what most of the spectators like to see.

Super Stocks formed another Spedeworth class. These had open wheels, but also had bumpers front

Below left: Custom Car magazine team driver Frank 'Fireball' Boyles, with his ultra-neat Midget

Below right: clearing away a Mini, prior to a Superstox race

still did happen. Engine capacity was limited to 1660 cc, and many drivers spent a great deal of money extracting the maximum horsepower from them. Most popular cars for this class were Escorts, although Anglias and Minis were also seen regularly. It was in hot-rod racing that big names were made and the big prize money won. George Polley, Mick Collard and ex-rally cross driver Barry Lee were all first-class drivers in hot rods, and had strong following around the country.

The British Stock Car Association, on the other hand, stuck more closely to the sport of stock-car racing in its original form. Their cars were also open

and rear to help one's competitors get out of the way. Engines used were the MGB 1800 cc and Ford 1600 GT units, front-mounted, and the rules dictate that some part of a saloon car must be present in the body. The racing in this class was very exciting and competitive, although, once again, the cars were not particularly expensive to build.

The class that gained most popularity in recent years, though, was hot-rod racing. Here, the bodies of the cars concerned were quite standard in appearance, although they rarely got as badly damaged as the stock cars. They had no bumpers, and in fact metal to metal contact was frowned on, although it

Above: unlike the 'Banger' and stock-car classes, the Hot Rods do not try to bash each other off the track, and when there is a coming together, many hearts stop!

wheelers with bodywork very largely handmade but containing a few token compound curves from production cars. Formula One was for cars with American V8 or Jaguar engines and Formula Two, that mainly operated in the West Country, was for cars of a lesser capacity.

Stock-car tracks were in all parts of the country from Cowdenbeath to St Austell in 1975 and, although attendances were not on the level of that meeting in New Cross in 1954, it was still an extremely popular form of motor sport and one which looked like being in vogue for as long as cars continued to outlive their usefulness for everyday driving on the road! AA

MOTORING JARGON is a dreadful jumble of popular and ill-chosen usage, and of all the morass of misleading expressions and half-understood connotations it embraces, the terminology of the drive line contains more than its fair share of vagueness and confusion. Consider the word *overdrive*: it means a gear ratio (within a gearbox) such that the speed of the output shaft in relation to that of the input shaft is in a ratio higher than unity—or lower, if you refuse to subscribe to the jargon; *and* it means a supplementary gearbox, usually but not necessarily epicyclic, downstream from the main gearbox and likewise offering a multiplication rather than a demultiplication of the latter's output shaft speed; *and* it means any overall gear ratio so high that the engine cannot reach the peak of its power curve. The facts that an overdrive gear speed need not have an overdrive effect, and that an overdrive effect can be achieved without recourse to overdrive gearing, suggest that the word is overworked.

To avoid unnecessary confusion, let us first ratify one piece of established jargon. The higher the numerical ratio of a reduction gear—that is, the slower the output shaft revolves for a given rate of input shaft revolution—the lower we consider the gear. Engineers outside the automotive world consider it higher; that is their problem, not ours. In our car's gearbox, bottom gear is the lowest, top gear the highest. If the overall ratio of top gear (taking into account the final drive or axle gearing and the rolling radius of the tyres) allows the engine speed, at which maximum power is developed, to correspond to the road speed at which the tractive effort at the driving wheels is the same as the sum of wind and mechanical resistance to motion, then the car is correctly geared to reach the highest speed of which it is capable. However, any trifling increase in resistance, be it of wind or gradient, will prevent the car from reaching its true maximum speed.

Car manufacturers long ago learnt that the reluctance of the average driver to explore the maximum-speed capability of his car was matched only by his reluctance to change down from top gear once he had engaged it. What people wanted was lively top-gear acceleration: the easy way to provide it was to lower the gearing (usually in the final drive) and so increase the torque multiplication. This produced two unwanted side-effects: the car was fussier at all speeds, because the engine would be working at a higher crankshaft rate for a given road speed, and there was some risk of the engine being overspeeded and perhaps endangered by the ease with which it would run beyond the speed at which it developed maximum power. Inevitably it would wear out more quickly if subjected to sustained high-speed cruising, for which top gear ought really to be higher, not lower: a top gear that was theoretically too high would prevent the car from reaching its proper maximum speed unless aided by a downhill gradient or a following wind. In that event, it would still be running within its normal safe working range, while at cruising speeds only slightly lower it would seem more at ease and consume less fuel.

For many years, these opposing requirements were compromised by making the third and fourth ratios of the conventional four-speed gearbox very 'close' or numerically similar. The car might be very nearly as fast in third as in fourth; it might even be faster, as in the case of certain Frazer Nash models of about 1930 and certain Citroën models thirty years later. The snag was that it was a four-speed car with virtually three-speed performance, as it were: a car with two top gears and two others. Restoration of acceleration and hill-climbing prowess called for another gear, and when the need was crucial and money was no object, a

THE CRUISING GEAR

Overdrive units have, to some extent, been replaced by a fifth gear, but they are still popular

Above: an external view of the type of Laycock-de Normanville overdrive unit fitted to the Triumph Dolomite; in fact, this company is responsible for most of the overdrives in use

five-speed gearbox could be made—as, to the consternation of their Grand Prix rivals, in the case of Delage whose high-revving 1926/7 straight-eight 1½-litre could peak at about 8000 rpm in fourth gear and then relax for the rest of any long straight (and straights, like races, were longer in those days) at 6500 in fifth.

In those days, as still today in many front-engined rear-drive cars, top gear was direct, a 1:1 ratio in which the output and input shafts of the gearbox were coupled together. This eliminated the frictional losses involved in the meshing gears of the lower ratios, and thus made top gear (which was most used) mechanically the most efficient. In a case such as that of the Delage, fifth gear would not be used much: it would be better to make the 'other top' gear, fourth, direct drive, and provide a geared-up fifth—an overdrive gear. The same solution had been found in other, earlier cases such as the Rolls-Royce Silver Ghost which, for a time, had a four-speed gearbox in which third was direct and fourth was geared up. Alas, Royce found that customers insisted on going everywhere in overdrive, which could be neither as quiet nor as lively as direct third, and he could not educate them to think of third as top when there was another higher ratio available!

By the 1930s, the American manufacturers were occasionally running into the same problems. A three-speed gearbox was the norm there, but some of the fastest cars needed more. The answer was to make two top gears available where they really counted—in the back axle—so that both were direct drive as far as the gearbox was concerned. The fact that the gear-change mechanism was clumsy and the extra unsprung

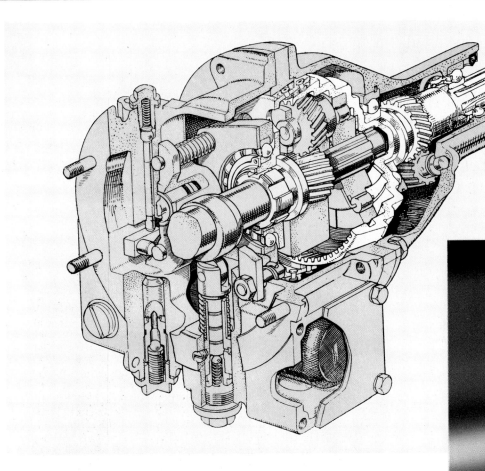

Below: the neat overdrive switch of the Triumph Dolomite Sprint, which is also used on the Triumph 2000/2500 series. Most overdrive switches in the past have been placed on stalks on the steering column, but this type has proved more popular as it can be used directly in conjunction with the gear lever

weight in the axle undesirable did not matter much to the average American, whose driving habits were such that he proved just as incorrigible as the average Rolls-Royce owner.

In another twenty years, the problems recurred, because new motorways, fuels, oils, bearings and tyres encouraged people to drive for long distances at or near maximum speed. To enable this to be done on the rising, rather than the drooping, portion of the power curve, a new apparatus became available. It was a two-speed epicyclic gearbox attached to the rear of a car's normal gearbox, providing a continuation of the direct drive line when all three elements of the gearset (sun gear, planetary pinions, and annulus or ring gear) were locked together by the hydraulically operated cone clutch, or a higher ratio when the clutch moved to lock the sun to the casing. The apparatus was known as the de Normanville (Captain de Normanville was the patentee) or more fully as the Laycock-de Normanville overdrive. It was little less than sensational at the time, featuring in the then new Austin-Healey 100, the Jensen and optionally in the popular Standard Vanguard; many other British cars, mainly of the high-performance type, soon acquired it as an option or even as standard equipment.

By the end of the decade, it had even reached foreign manufacturers. Ferrari used it in the 250 GT 2+2 model that appeared in 1960—but as was too often the case with Ferrari engineering at that time, the installation was botched. It was a feature of the Laycock mechanism that the hydraulic operation of its clutch employed oil from a supply shared with the gearbox and pressurised by an integral pump worked by an eccentric on the overdrive input shaft. In the Ferrari, the gearbox had to be filled with an oil that was suitable for the overdrive; alternatively, the latter had to suffer an unsuitable oil to preserve the gearbox. No good could come of such an arrangement.

Above: most overdrive units consist of an epicyclic gear train, operated either hydraulically or mechanically; this cutaway shows a Laycock-de Normanville overdrive, which is characterised by its hydraulic clutch operation. The shaft from the gearbox is shown in red, while the output shaft to the wheels is in blue. In overdrive, movement is transmitted through the gear train, while in direct drive, the clutch (in green), which is splined to the input shaft, presses against the gear housing and locks input against output

In Britain, the Laycock-de Normanville overdrive went from strength to strength. It was soon realised that the overdrive could be made operable while one of the indirect ratios of the gearbox was engaged, thus acting as a ratio-splitter: with careful juggling of cog sizes in the gearbox, a fairly regular progression might be contrived in which overdrive third nicely bridged the gap between direct third and top, overdrive second doing the same between direct second and third. Thus a four-speed gearbox might be made part of a seven-speed transmission. It was never thought safe to apply the overdrive to first gear, for the ratio of first was invariably so low as to multiply the torque of the engine three or more times, the resulting output torque from the gearbox being too much for the overdrive to stand. When allied to large engines, the overdrive might not be able to take the torque in second gear either, and in really lusty machines, it was thought more prudent to limit its operation to top gear only. All this could be arranged with the aid of simple electrical switches tripped by the gearbox selector rods, for the driver's control over the overdrive was by means of an electrical two-position switch whose circuit could be interrupted by the gearbox switches if the wrong gear were engaged. In the appropriate gear, all the driver had to do was flick his control switch (which might be on the facia or the steering column, and later found favour in the knob on the gearlever) and the job was done. There was no need to touch the clutch, although in some installations the change up into overdrive would not be made unless the overdrive were temporarily relieved of full-throttle torque. The simple treatment was briefly to release the accelerator—just as a brief blip of the throttle would smooth a downward change from overdrive to direct top, without any of the clutch-dipping practised by so many drivers.

Bearing in mind the simplicity of the electrical circuit, which had to do no more than operate a solenoid controlling the valve which admitted high-pressure oil to shift the cone clutch to the overdrive position, it is amazing how little thought went into most installations. It was too easy for a driver to slow down in overdrive top gear, select perhaps first or second gear, and then when accelerating hard again

substitute for it. Two exceptions to this generality that spring to mind were the MG and Triumph sports cars, in which the overdrive compensated for the shortcomings of gearboxes that were never designed for anything but placid family saloons, with ratios much too wide to suit sporting driving.

Here lies a hint to the gradual disappearance of the epicyclic overdrive unit. While gearboxes were in production that needed its help, it enjoyed a steady demand but, although the cost of retooling to make a five-speed gearbox might be greater than the cost of buying and fitting a heavy and complex (and therefore expensive) Laycock overdrive, sooner or later every gearbox has to make way for a new design. When that happens, the obvious course is to make a five-speed

Left: motoring journalist Roger Bell, with his Group One Triumph Dolomite Sprint, at Britain's Thruxton circuit. These cars dominate their class not only because their 'standard' 2-litre engines produce almost 200 bhp, but because as the cars have overdrive systems, they virtually have six-speed gearboxes. Overdrive-third is particularly useful; this gear is higher than direct third and lower than direct fourth, and 'bridges' the gap

and passing from third to the top gear he expected, to find instead that overdrive was back in use and the engine revs had slumped. If overdrive were effective in third gear as well as fourth, then the sudden abatement of acceleration would be felt when changing up from second. Such oversights were still thus rewarded in many cars made years later.

Perhaps the reason was a revulsion from the elaborate and ill-reasoned (not to mention frequently maladjusted) system of kick-downs, drop-outs and inhibitors that made the use of overdrive in the original Austin-Healey unnecessarily complicated and the use of the later Borg-Warner overdrive (an unsuccessful attempt to rival Laycock) impossibly unpredictable. In fact, very little complexity was involved in providing a solution to the problem of the recurrent overdrive: as apparently only Bristol had the wit to demonstrate, in their 405 model first shown late in 1954, all that was needed was a simple relay. When overdrive top was engaged and the driver changed down (or even merely moved the gearlever into the neutral position) the gearbox switch isolated the driver's relay switch, which snapped back into the normal position; next time top gear was engaged, it would be direct top. Obviously such a system could only work when overdrive was limited to top gear, as in the Bristol, but the objection was more imaginary than real, for in most other installations overdrive third is so similar to direct top as to constitute a somewhat useless (and mechanically less efficient)

gearbox replace the old four-speeder, and by the middle 1960s there were many European manufacturers who had done just that. Fifth gear might be, and usually was, an overdrive ratio in the sense of being geared higher than 1:1. Occasionally, as in the Getrag gearbox adopted for the Jensen-Healey and optional in the BMW 2002, fifth is direct and the final-drive gearing (or the tyre size) may be altered to give an overdrive effect if desired.

In fact, it is really immaterial whether the highest gear is direct or not, save in the sense that a direct drive is more efficient than an indirect one. If a gearbox has a direct-drive ratio, all the others it offers must lose some power transmission efficiency through at least two pairs of meshing gears; whereas if all the gears are indirect, with the output shaft not coaxial with the input, each ratio involves only one pair of meshing gears, so all are of roughly equal efficiency. All-indirect gearboxes are not uncommon in front-wheel-drive cars, and are the rule in rear-engined cars —and when a gearbox is all-indirect it matters not at all whether any given ratio is higher or lower than unity. All that matters is the overall transmission ratio, from engine to wheels: in such a car, a gear can only be described as an overdrive if it is (however deliberately) too high. There is hope for the language yet— but if early pioneers of overdrive had been less obsessed by mechanics and had called the thing a cruising gear, it and the customers would have given far less trouble.　　　　　　　　　　　　　　LJKS

PASSING IN SAFETY

To make good progress on the road, it is necessary to overtake, but there is a right way and a wrong way of doing this

OVERTAKING IS PROBABLY the most hazardous of all motoring manoeuvres. At the same time, it is also the one manoeuvre that sets a hallmark on driving and shows whether the person behind the wheel is a good driver or just someone who can move a vehicle from point A to point B. The laws governing overtaking differ from country to country, from state to state. Basically, however, overtaking is merely a matter of common sense.

The art of overtaking is, as in all driving, that of making quick and correct decisions, all of which must be carried out with deliberation. A driver with a negative attitude will sooner or later hesitate at the crucial moment, possibly with fatal results.

Among the points to remember when overtaking is that it should never be attempted when approaching a pedestrian crossing, a road junction, a corner or bend, the brow of a hill or on a hump-backed bridge. Nor should overtaking be attempted where a road narrows, or where to do so would cause another vehicle to swerve or reduce speed. In addition, it should never be attempted where there is a double white line on the road or where the line on your side of the road is continuous. All these points are pure common sense.

Overtaking must always be accomplished in the minimum of time, so leaving the road clear for others who may be travelling in the opposite direction or behind you. And to this end the most important consideration is that of the position of your vehicle both on the road and in relation to the vehicle to be overtaken. Too many motorists are like rabbits: they sit right up tight behind the vehicle in front, popping out to see if the road is clear, then popping back when they find it is not.

If a car driver positions himself some 20 feet behind a lorry he wishes to overtake, he will lose sight of the nearside kerb just in front of the lorry and lose sight of the offside of the road about 150 feet beyond it. In a position 90 feet behind the lorry, the driver will command a view of about 100 feet along the nearside and a very good view along the offside, a position that both secures a good overall vision of the road and, at the same time, indicates whether it is safe to overtake.

The really good driver will not only hang well back from the vehicle ahead but will also change his point of view before actually overtaking. From a position close to the nearside kerb he will have an unobstructed view along the nearside of the road, and if the road is clear he will then move out towards the crown of the road, getting a long clear view of the offside of the road and any oncoming traffic. If all is clear he can go ahead and overtake in safety. If it is not clear he can hang back and wait, relying on the maxim of 'whenever in doubt, hang back'.

The essence of good driving is to ensure that you are always in the right position on the road, travelling at the right speed for the conditions at that particular time and with the right gear engaged for that speed—and this is never more important than during overtaking. Never find yourself in the situation where you have to change down a gear whilst actually overtaking. Once you have had a good look at the road, and decided it is clear and safe to overtake, select the correct gear and accelerate smoothly and quickly clear of the hazard. Make the arc of overtaking long and shallow rather than short and sharp and do not pop out from immediately behind the vehicle ahead, overtake then cut sharply back in front of the overtaken vehicle. By extending and flattening the arc, much less steering effort will be required and much more directional stability will be retained.

Never overtake if it means you are going to be the meat in the sandwich. In other words, never attempt to overtake a vehicle if it means that, whilst you are actually alongside the vehicle you are overtaking, another vehicle coming in the opposite direction passes you. The slightest of changes in direction by either of them, a sudden gust of wind or even one of the drivers sneezing, and you could be in serious physical danger. If in doubt, hang back.   FP

Below: following another vehicle too closely is not only unnecessary, but also very dangerous. Here, in picture A, the driver of the car is following the lorry too closely, and there is quite a large 'blind' spot, shown by the blue area. In picture B, however, the car driver holds back and can see further down the road for oncoming cars as well as seeing more of the pavement and being able to watch for errant pedestrians. The arrows show the smoothest path a driver can take to pass the obstruction and, as can be seen, the line is much sharper in the picture labelled A

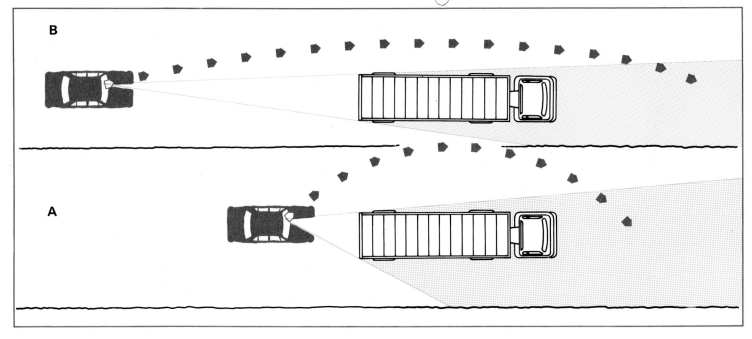

A BRITISH MOTORING ENIGMA

E. H. Owen is said to have manufactured cars in Kensington, but there is no evidence of this

'THEN,' SAID SHERLOCK HOLMES, 'there was the curious incident of the dog in the night time'.

'But the dog did nothing in the night time,' countered Doctor Watson.

'That is the curious incident,' replied Holmes.

However, far more curious still is the question of what E. H. Owen, of Carrick House, Comeragh Road, Kensington, West London, did from 1899 to 1935 for, although he was nominally in business to manufacture and sell motor cars, there is no concrete evidence to prove that he did either of these things at any time. His name, and details of the curious range of vehicles he offered, bob in and out of sight in various reference lists of the period like corks in a mill-race, yet it seems impossible to find any one of the cars offered for sale in classified or display advertising of the period.

Owen claimed to have offered a 10 hp shaft-driven twin-cylinder model as early as 1899, but as the claim was not made until the 1920s, the existence of this vehicle at such an early date must be regarded as, at best, apochryphal.

In 1901, Owen advertised that he was taking orders for the Twentieth Century Voiturette, available with engines of 9, 12, 16 or 24 hp, but no orders (or cars) seem to have materialised, and nothing was heard from Comeragh Road until 1905–06, when a range of four vehicles was offered. These were the 10 hp Parisia, the 20 hp Londinia, the 30 hp Twentieth Century and the 40 hp Owen's Gearless; somewhere along the line, Atalanta, Italiana and Lococar models were also offered, as well as Owen's Petelectra (with a petrol-electric transmission). From this assortment of unlikely titles, it seems more than probable that Mr Owen's idea of motor manufacture was to buy complete vehicles from some obscure maker and put his own badge on the radiator.

However, from 1907 on, the picture becomes more eccentric. That year, Owen listed four models, of 25, 35, 40 and 50 hp. The 25 hp, with a 5276 cc four-cylinder engine, cost £375, the 5883 cc 35 hp six was £500, the 6435 cc 40 hp four was £750 and the 50 hp, with a 7915 cc six-cylinder power unit, was paradoxically cheaper than the 40 hp, retailing at £675. So was Mr Owen buying somebody else's chassis and re-badging? It seems likely, except that quoted cylinder dimensions and, more importantly, prices, do not tie up with any other likely product from any other maker.

For instance, the 25 hp had similar cylinder dimensions to the contemporary 25/30 Austin (£600), 30 hp Belsize (£540) and 20 hp Itala (£750), but does not agree on grounds of cost with any of them. The 35 hp six-cylinder Owen had a similar bore and stroke to the 35 hp Belsize—but the latter car was £800. The 40 hp compared with the Napier 45—and was £50 dearer, while the 50 might (or most probably might not) have been a small-bore version of the 60 hp Belsize (£1000).

Indeed, it is odd how the 1907 Owens compare with

OWEN "EIGHT."

8-cyl., V type, 75 × 150 mm., 5,302 c.c.   Tax, £28. Dual, Owen starter, Owen carb.   Single-plate clutch, 2-speed sliding gears, spiral bevel drive.   Disc detach. wheels, 895 × 135 tyres.   Semi-elliptic front and rear springs.   4ft. 10in. track, 16ft. 10in. overall. Clearance, 9in.   Weight (chassis),   1 ton 2 cwt. Petrol, 30 gallons ; consumption, 15 m.p.g. Price : Chassis, £2,250.

the contemporary Belsize range for cylinder dimensions, if not price, but then the 1908 prices upset any comfortable theories of any collusion between the makes, unless Belsize were operating on an astronomical retail profit margin, which seems unlikely. The 1908 3922 cc Owen four cost £295, while a Belsize with identical bore and stroke was £360; the 5883 cc Owen six was down to £395, while the comparable Belsize was now £525. There was a new long-stroke 6855 cc 40 hp four-cylinder Owen (£650) which did not seem to have any equivalent anywhere among the many makes on the market, and the 50 hp six now cost only £495.

Now Owen prices went in all directions: the 1909 20 hp was up to £330, the 40 hp fell to £485, and there was a monstrous (and ephemeral) 10,283 cc six with the same bore and stroke as the 40 hp.

Next year, there was a new 15 hp four of 2540 cc (£330), a new 5817 cc 40 hp four (£450) and an 8727 cc six, also new, which had a stroke of almost seven inches. The same three cars were listed in 1911, when the 15 hp was £375, the 35 (ex-40 hp) was £460 and the 60 £675.

Thereafter came a lull in Mr Owen's high-powered inertia, interrupted only by a world war and the re-numbering of Carrick House from 72 to 6 Comeragh Road. But in 1920, this seller of dreams—for from their prices, his 1905–11 offerings must have been figments of his imagination or altruism carried to

Above: this photograph of an Owen Eight is from the April 1921 *Autocar Buyers' Guide.* Could it be a Kenworthy or another make?

Previous page, top: probably the only illustration of an 'Owen' other than the *Autocar* picture is this drawing from the *Motor-Car Journal* of 30 March 1901 showing the 'Twentieth Century' voiturette

Previous page, bottom: a picture taken in 1975 of the supposed Owen premises at No 6 Comeragh Road, West Kensington. Was it possible that cars were ever made there?

impossible ends—re-entered the sales lists with the Orleans car (no relation to the New Orleans which had been built at Twickenham pre-war), which was offered right up to 1935 in 12 hp and 20 hp forms, the smaller car costing (1926–27) £395 and the larger (1926–27) £650 as a tourer, £750 as a saloon. Then the Owen re-surfaced, seemingly in the guise of a small-bore (2994 cc) version of the 1909 40 hp power unit, but endowed with only one forward speed, which seems to have been carrying freedom from gear-changing too far! There was also a suppositious 40 hp petrol-electric priced at £1100, but both these chimerae vanished in 1921, replaced by a 5302 cc V8 of probable American antecedents, with only two forward gears and a price tag of £2250 for the bare chassis, £150 more than a Rolls Silver Ghost or a Napier 40/50.

The old 60 hp tag was revived in 1925, for a straight-eight of 7634 cc with a £1750 price tag (more than an Hispano-Suiza or a Bentley), which lasted until 1928 or 1936, depending on which classification list you believe. The post-war V8 is reputed to have resembled the contemporary American Kenworthy, but the Line O'Eight Kenworthy was one of America's first straight-eights.

So, was E. H. Owen a charlatan? Did he ever sell a car? Was it all a hoax? One thing alone is certain: there can be no tidy answer for this, one of motoring history's most curious enigmas.   DBW

BEFORE THE DAYS of the automatic gearbox, the petrol-electric transmission enjoyed a certain vogue, for it eliminated the need to acquire the somewhat complex skills of changing gear silently with a non-synchromesh transmission; but if the petrol-electric was easy to use, it was also expensive to build, bulky and heavy, which made it more suitable for commercial vehicles (of which the most notable example was the Tilling-Stevens) than for the private car. There were one or two notable exceptions to this general rule, however, and one of the more ingenious electric transmissions was conceived just before World War I by Ray M. Owen of the Baker, Rauch & Lang company of Cleveland, Ohio, who were renowned for their Baker and Raulang battery electric cars. He adapted the Entz transmission, which was designed for use in the new generation of oil-engined battleships (such as the 1919 *New Mexico*), for automotive use, and began production of a luxury car with this form of drive in 1914.

Under its original name of Owen Magnetic, the 'Car of a Thousand Speeds' does not seem to have been too successful, but by 1920 J. L. Crown had taken over the design rights, and was producing cars in a factory at Wilkes-Barre, Pennsylvania. Crown, it appears, was more interested in the European market than the American, for in the autumn of 1920 he arrived in England with a 38hp Owen Magnetic touring car, and he then set about selling the manufacturing rights.

W. Harold Johnson of *Conquest* magazine took the Owen-Magnetic, which was fitted with a 6864 cc ohv six-cylinder engine, for a trial run. He wrote, 'Except for its transmission system (a very big exception) the car is a conventional member of the highest class of petrol propelled vehicles. The engine is large—38 hp—and the car itself is big. On the road it has all the characteristics that one expects to find in a car which is both luxurious and expensive.

'Instead of the ordinary clutch, the flywheel carries, on an extension of its flange, a set of electro-magnets. On the end of the propeller shaft and between these magnets is mounted an armature, and just behind this armature is situated a second. Obviously, if either of these armatures be compelled to revolve the propeller shaft revolves with them, or, conversely, whenever the car is moving along the road these two armatures are also revolving. Around the first armature, the field magnets on the flywheel revolve whenever the engine is turning. Around the second armature is placed a second set of field magnets, which are bolted rigidly to a casing, and cannot revolve under any circumstances. ... Assume that the engine is started and that the car is stationary, the magnets of the first of the two electrical units mentioned are now revolving round their armature, which is, of course, stationary. The result is the generation of current, the unit forming an ordinary electric dynamo. But, besides generating current, the two units of the primary motor, or dynamo, are exercising a mutual drag, and there is a tendency for the rotating magnets to pull the armature round with them. Now suppose it is desired to start the car.

'The controlling switch is put in such a position that the current generated by what may be termed the slipping between rotating magnets and the armature is directed to the secondary motor. As soon as the magnets of this unit are energised, the armature is made to revolve, so that there are two forces at work, both tending to turn the propeller shaft and so propel the car.

'The first is the magnetic drag between the two

units of the first motor. The second is the ordinary electric motor action in the secondary motor. The practical effect of putting the switch into the number one position of the quadrant on the steering wheel is that the car will almost imperceptibly move forward.'

The speed control quadrant was calibrated to show a 'charging' position, in which the engine could be run while the car was at a standstill to top up the 24 volt starting and lighting batteries; a 'starting' position, in which current from these batteries was used to spin the engine via the primary motor; 'neutral' and six speeds forward, in which the current supplied to the secondary motor was progressively reduced, until, in 'high', the rotating magnets and their armature were magnetically locked together and no current

'CAR OF 1000 SPEEDS'

With the Entz magnetic transmission, the Owen Magnetic was a smooth car with easily adjustable 'gear ratios'

Top: the Owen Magnetic in British Crown Magnetic form; this car was powered by a 6864 cc 38 hp engine

Above: An Owen Magnetic with rear-seat passenger 'touched in'

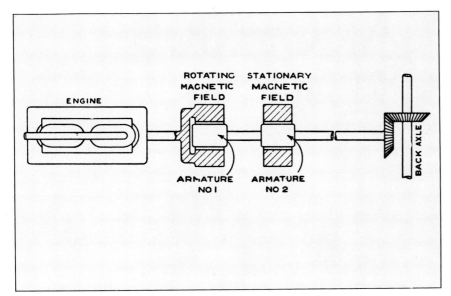

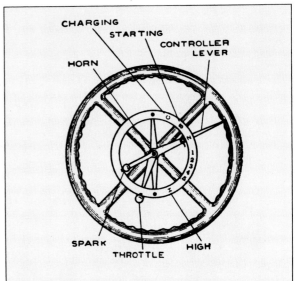

was passing to the secondary unit. In fact, as there was no mechanical connection between magnets and armature, there was a perceptible amount of slip between them. Oddly enough, tests showed that whether the engine was turning at 1000 or 3000 rpm, there was always a difference of 80 rpm between flywheel speed and armature speed. Or, as W. Harold Johnson put it: 'When the car is on the road, there is a delightful absence of that sense of friction that is always more or less present in the transmission system of an ordinary car'.

Another advantage was that the car could coast once it had gathered sufficient momentum, or was running downhill, with consequent fuel economies. If the car was put into 'neutral' while coasting, the motors were converted into a powerful electromagnetic brake, which became ineffective below 15 mph so that it could never cause the wheels to lock and skid. The braking effect also came into action when the car was starting on a hill, so that it could not run backwards.

A separate gearbox gave a reverse gear (in which all speeds were theoretically available) and an emergency low. But when Crown began production (and changed the car's name to Crown Magnetic) the emergency low was omitted, which proved to be a big mistake, for even with aluminium tourer bodywork and wings the car scaled over two-and-a-half tons in going order, which meant that on a long steep hill, the force of gravity could defeat that 'magnetic drag' and bring the car to an ignominious standstill—as indeed happened when the Crown Magnetic was being demonstrated to some Welsh businessmen who, it was hoped, might finance its production in Britain.

W. Harold Johnson demonstrated this drawback in a more amusing fashion: 'The switch on the steering wheel was put in the 'number one' position (there being no occupant of the driving seat) and, as the car moved forward, I walked to the front of it, placed my hand and my weight against the radiator, and held the car stationary. Then I moved away and, as I did so, the car gradually moved forward again.'

J. L. Crown then fitted the Owen Magnetic transmission to a number of Minerva cars; these transmissions were built to his order by Greenwood & Batley of Leeds, better-known as makers of electric milk floats.

Another company which used the Owen transmission at this period was Magnetic Cars of Chelsea, who used this car in a chassis powered by the same Burt-McCollum single-sleeve-valve engines as the Argyll:

Above: a simplified diagram of the ENTZ magnetic transmission system used in the Owen Magnetic; armature dynamo, while No 2 constitutes an electric motor

Above right: the control system for the transmission was fitted to the steering wheel; the 'gear lever' incorporated positions for charging the battery, starting the engine, neutral and six forward speeds

the marque's life was short, obscure and unsuccessful.

Next, Crown joined forces with the British Ensign company of Willesden, run by Edward Gillett: in July 1923 he and the company's chief engineer, T. E. B. James took an American-built Owen Magnetic on a sales tour across Europe. The handsome vee-radiator boiled crossing the Mont Cenis Pass, and the car was involved in a traffic incident in Modane; neither Fiat nor Isotta-Fraschini were interested in taking up the engineering rights, and all in all the trip was an expensive waste of time.

British Ensign had already built one Ensign Magnetic, using their existing luxury chassis, which had an ohv 6105 cc engine developing over 100 bhp. Now they began work on a second, which was intended for one of their directors, a Welshman named Rees, who was also manager of the Glanmore Foundry of Llanelly: Rees had lost a leg in an accident at the foundry, and reckoned that the Ensign Magnetic, with its steering-wheel controls and only two pedals, was just the car for him.

But as work started, J. L. Crown decided that there was no future in magnetic transmissions: he withdrew his capital from British Ensign and took it over to Germany, where he made a fortune dealing in the fallen Mark, and used it to buy up a number of properties, including a large hotel.

T. E. B. James finished Rees's car amid an atmosphere of gloom: British Ensign were virtually broke, and had dismissed most of their staff. One or two Owen Magnetics, including one belonging to General Ironside, came in for repair, and there was a desultory attempt at building a sub-utility £100 car, the Gillett, but there was obviously no future for the company, even as a magnetic transmission repair specialists, and they closed down.

In any case, there was little market for a car of this complexity at a chassis price of virtually £2000; although the transmission was generally reliable, except for a tendency to burn out the ball-bearing at the front end of the propeller shaft, customers were wary of having to employ a qualified electrical engineer as chauffeur.

The American end of the operation was dead already—Crown had closed down the Wilkes-Barre works soon after he came to Europe—and with the bankruptcy of the Willesden company the story of the 'wonderful car . . . that a baby, a country yokel, or a Brooklands racing expert may all start . . . with equal smoothness' came to an anticlimactic end.   DBW

Motor racing's pace-setter

THE BRAZILIANS take their sport very seriously, and when Carlos Pace (pronounced Par-chay) drove his Brabham to victory in the 1975 Brazilian Grand Prix, they gave their fellow countryman a rapturous welcome. They literally tore him out of the car and hoisted him shoulder-high to receive their appreciation. It was a moving moment for the young man from São Paolo. Not only was it a GP win in front of his home crowd, but it was his first World Championship Grand Prix win ever.

Pace's first GP victory was a long time coming. Born on 6 October 1944, he was the son of a fairly wealthy man. At the age of sixteen, Carlos bought a 125cc go-kart. He then proceeded to win six races, to finish second in the Brazilian championship. A certain Wilson Fittipaldi finished fourth. He continued to race karts for a further two years and in 1963 began his car-racing career by entering a 1-litre DKW in the inaugural Interlagos race. He proved so impressive in practice that he was offered a Team Willys Renault Dauphine Gordini for the race proper. He finished in second place and this persuaded Team Willys to continue to support him. Their faith paid off because by 1965 Carlos had become Brazilian Saloon Car Champion. Two years later, Pace became the Brazilian National Champion and this time the runner-up position went to a young driver named Emerson Fittipaldi. Pace then consolidated his position as Brazil's number one driver by taking the national title again in 1968, driving a prototype Bino, and once more in 1969, this time behind the wheel of an Alfa Romeo T33.

By this time, however, Emerson Fittipaldi had arrived in Britain and was causing a sensation with his incredibly fast and tidy driving style.

It was Fittipaldi, in fact, who helped Pace arrange a Jim Russell Lotus 59 Formula Three drive when he too arrived in Britain at the end of 1969. From this moment onwards, Pace, in spite of his more successful record in Brazil, was forced to live under the shadow of Fittipaldi. Nevertheless, it did not affect either their friendship or Pace's driving, and he went on to become the Forward Trust Formula Three Champion for 1970. By now, Pace's talent had become obvious and in 1971 he was signed by Frank Williams to drive his March 712 Formula Two cars. It proved a troublesome period for Carlos, however, and he managed only one win, during the season, at Imola.

In 1972, Frank Williams invited Pace to join his Formula One team, driving the rather out-dated March 721. Try as they may, neither Williams nor Pace could get the cars to work effectively, although Carlos did manage a sixth at the Spanish GP and a fifth at the Belgium GP. The season, however, was not a total loss as he was asked to drive a works F2 Surtees car during the second half of the season. This in turn led to an offer from the works Ferrari team to join their sports-car effort. Driving a Ferrari 312P, and sharing with Austrian Helmut Marko, he finished second in the Österreichring 1000 km, and proved that given competitive machinery, he was a force to be reckoned with.

The following season, 1973, saw Pace sign for the Surtees team alongside the equally promising Jochen Mass. At last, Pace was an accepted member of the top class of motor racing and it seemed as though it would not be too long before the talented Brazilian won his first Grand Prix.

Left and below: Jose Carlos Pace in the Brabham BT44, the car with which he secured his first GP win, at Interlagos, Brazil, in 1975

Alas, it was not to be. Time and time again mechanical failure put him out of the race and his best results were a fourth at the German Grand Prix and a third at the Austrian GP. One consolation, however, was setting the fastest lap during the German GP at Nürburgring, traditionally the most demanding and difficult circuit of them all. During this season, he also continued his association with the Ferrari sports-car team and enjoyed some good results. Sharing the car with Arturo Merzario, he finished second at the Nürburgring 1000km and at Le Mans, third at Watkins Glen and fourth at Vallelunga, Dijon and Spa.

Despite the setbacks of his previous F1 season, Pace signed with Surtees for the 1974 season. A fourth in Brazil augured well for the season but once again it was not to be. 1974 was a troubled time for the Surtees team. During the season they lost their sponsorship and the consequent lack of finance severely hampered the team. By the time seven Grands Prix had been run, Pace could take no more and quit the team.

It was not very long before he was back behind the wheel, however. Shortly afterwards, he was signed by the works Brabham team. At last, Carlos had a car equal to his ability and he was not slow to take his opportunity. In the Italian GP, he finished fifth and ended the season with a second at Watkins Glen.

For 1975, Brabham designer Gordon Murray updated the Brabham BT44 and gave works drivers Carlos Reutmann and Carlos Pace a thoroughly competitive motor car. In the first race of the season, the Argentine GP, Pace put his car on the front row of the grid but was forced to retire in the race. His second race was the Brazilian GP and it was here that Pace won his first GP, and wrote his name into the history books of Brazil.   MW

FINE ENGINEERING, LONG LIFE AND LUXURY

Until the merger in 1954 with Studebaker, Packard was the only truly independent American car manufacturer intent on building luxury limousines

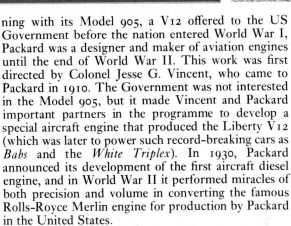

ONE OF THE GREATEST NAMES in car building in the history of the United States, Packard stood for fine engineering, long life, great 12-cylinder luxury cars, early racing success and, in its last years, technical innovation. Clearly identified by their yoke-shaped radiators and fluted hoods, Packards projected an aura of prestige and excellence (especially in the years between the two World Wars) that was unmatched by any other make in North America. Indeed, in most of the years from World War I until its merger with Studebaker in 1954, a span of more than thirty years, Packard was America's only entirely independent auto company dedicated exclusively to the manufacture of the finest possible cars. For this reason, and also for its accomplishments in the design and production of aircraft engines, Packard was the only company in the United States whose work could be favourably compared with that of England's Rolls-Royce organisation.

From 1899, when the first Packard car was completed, until the last one was made in 1958, the company produced 1,610,890 automobiles. Its largest production in one year was 109,518 in 1937, approached, but not equalled, by the best post-World War II year in 1948, in which 104,593 Packards were sold. Less famed was Packard's production of trucks, amounting to 43,484 units from 1908 to 1923. Begin-

ning with its Model 905, a V12 offered to the US Government before the nation entered World War I, Packard was a designer and maker of aviation engines until the end of World War II. This work was first directed by Colonel Jesse G. Vincent, who came to Packard in 1910. The Government was not interested in the Model 905, but it made Vincent and Packard important partners in the programme to develop a special aircraft engine that produced the Liberty V12 (which was later to power such record-breaking cars as *Babs* and the *White Triplex*). In 1930, Packard announced its development of the first aircraft diesel engine, and in World War II it performed miracles of both precision and volume in converting the famous Rolls-Royce Merlin engine for production by Packard in the United States.

However, Packard was a car company first and foremost, upholding—until its last hours—the traditions of excellence that dated from its very founding. The creator of the Packard car was James Ward Packard, whose New York and Ohio Company, in Warren, Ohio, was a maker of electrical equipment at the turn of the century. Like many engineers of his time, he was intrigued by the new-fangled motor vehicle and first had bought a French De Dion Bouton tricycle and then, in 1898, one of the first production cars made, in nearby Cleveland, Ohio, by

Below left: a 1903 Model C, which had a top speed of 40 mph and cost $3000. An example of this type was driven from San Francisco to New York in 61 days by drivers Fetch and Krarup

Below: a 1908 type 30 touring model

the flamboyant Alexander Winton. Driving the fifty miles home to Warren, Packard suffered numerous troubles with his new car. When he sought satisfaction from Winton, the rebuff he received was enough to start him working on a car design of his own. With the help of his brother, William Doud Packard, and two top-flight men he hired from Winton, he produced his first car in the next fourteen months. It ran for the first time on the streets of Warren on 6 November 1899.

This first car, appropriately named the Model A, had the high wire wheels tiller steering and single-cylinder engine, mounted under the seat, that were all typical of such early American cars as Ford, Cadillac and Oldsmobile. Unusual was its automatic spark advance, a Packard invention. Packard had no trouble selling this first car (for $1250), and set up an automobile division before the turn of the century to start producing Packards. He exhibited three cars at the first New York Show, in 1900, and in 1901 began equipping his cars with steering wheels, among the first in America to do so. From the A, he progressed to the Models B, C and F by 1902, still of the simple single-cylinder design that Packard favoured. He felt that four-cylinder cars just had four times as many things to go wrong.

Packard's jump not only to four but soon to twelve cylinders was the inspiration of Henry B. Joy, a

wealthy Detroit manufacturer who went to the New York Show in 1901, looking for a producer of horseless carriages to buy. Stopping at several agencies, Joy, and his brother-in-law, T. H. Newberry, chanced on the Ohio-built Packard and liked it. Joy bought one and, after driving it in Detroit, he negotiated, with Newberry and seven other associates, to buy a controlling interest in The Packard Motor Car Company (as it had been reformed in 1900). Although James Packard remained president of the firm when the Joy group took control, he decided to remain in Warren when the company's plant was moved to Detroit in 1903. He kept that post until 1909, staying as board chairman until 1912. He had kept his electrical equipment firm in existence separately and this ultimately became the Packard Electric Division of General Motors. According to Packard legend, James Packard was the man

Top: the first V12 built by Packard in 1915

Centre: the Packard V12 that achieved a speed of 149.87 mph on Daytona Beach in 1919. The official land-speed record at that time was 124 mph, but the 14,830 cc Packard's speed was never officially recognised

Above: a 1912 six-cylinder

Above: a 1928 Packard
526 convertible coupé,
powered by a 6.3-litre
106 bhp straight-eight
engine

who endowed the young auto company with the advertising slogan that became world-famous: 'Ask the man who owns one'.

Henry Joy, an energetic individual who fought hard on behalf of the new auto industry for good roads and freedom from arbitrary restrictions, also put Packard on a new road. Completed in 1904, the new Packard plant in Detroit was the first designed for car production by a young architect, Louis Kahn, who would become famous for his work in this field. The first four-cylinder Packard appeared in 1903, the Model K, and was the work of a French designer hired by Joy, Charles Schmidt. In the same year, Packard set up the first factory school in auto engineering, with regular classes for employees, and soon expanded it to give a one-month course in car maintenance and repair to Packard owners and chauffeurs. In those early years, Packard also developed a sales policy, unusual in the United States, that would distinguish it in later years. It tended to establish factory-owned distributorships and dealerships in key locations, instead of selling through independent dealers, as most others did. While other companies were paid for a car when it left the factory, Packard often did not collect until, much later, a retail sale was made. Larger amounts of capital investment were needed to work this way, and also to make many more parts of the car in Packard's own factory to keep its standards of quality as high as they had been in the past.

In 1904, designer Schmidt produced the Model L

Packard. This was historic, being the first Packard car to have the characteristic yoke-shaped radiator, with fluted hood corners, that was visible in all but the very last cars to bear the Packard name. It was also the first to show another Packard hallmark, indented hexagonal designs in the centre of each hub cap, later typically painted red. Becoming more and more prominent as a maker of luxury cars, Joy added a six to the Packard line in 1912. In the meantime, the fours had shown sparkling pace in competition, beginning with the special *Grey Wolf* built on a Model K chassis in 1904. This clocked 77.8 mph that year to set records at Daytona, and was placed fourth overall in the first Vanderbilt Cup Race in 1904.

Alvan Macauley, who formed the Packard car in his own image, came to the company as its general manager in 1910 and moved up to its presidency in 1916 when Henry Joy resigned; he was upset because his associates had voted against selling Packard to the men who created the Nash Motors Company instead. Joy, Macauley and engineer Jesse Vincent had been the architects of the car that was to put Packard on the map of motoring for all time, the sensational Twin Six of 1915. While others were debating over four, six and eight cylinders as the proper number for a luxury car, Packard leapfrogged them all with a 12-cylinder engine, introduced in May 1915 for the 1916 model year. Although not the first such engine, the Packard twelve was the first of its type to be built in large numbers for cars. So successful was it that almost half

the firm's 1916 output of 18,572 cars was accounted for by twelves. That was double the previous year's production, and the sales and profits (more than $6 million) doubled too with the Twin Six launching.

Built through the 1922 model year, the twelve kept its original dimensions of 76.2 × 127 mm for 6950 cc. Although it had only three main bearings and a slender crankshaft, the L-head engine had roller tappets and could rev smoothly to 3000 rpm, which was its maximum. It drove through a multi-disc clutch to a three-speed gearbox (little needed because it could accelerate smoothly from 3 mph in top gear) and a 4.36:1 rear axle. Prices ranged from $2600 for a touring car to $4600 for the Imperial Limousine on the long 135 inch wheelbase. During this first incarnation of its Twin Six, Packard made 35,046 such cars, beautiful big automobiles which were favoured by tycoons, by royalty, and even by Presidents. Warren G. Harding was the first US President to be driven in an automobile to his inauguration—in a Twin Six Packard.

Just before the US entered World War I, Packard built two special racing cars, both with V12 engines specially designed for aviation use. Both were driven by Ralph DePalma, the smaller one with a 299 cu in engine to successes in 1917 and 1918, and then to sixth at Indianapolis in 1919. Built strictly as a record-breaker, the larger car used the Model 905 aero engine, ahead of a central seat and tapered tail, to set a flying mile record of 149.9 mph at Daytona in 1919. Even more impressive was an average of 92.71 mph for the standing-start mile, a figure that stood as a US unlimited record for more than thirty years and was not bettered officially by a European car until 1929. These racers, Enzo Ferrari wrote, helped inspire him to make his own twelve-cylindered cars: 'I had always hankered after a 12-cylinder engine, recalling early photographs I had seen of a Packard that had raced at Indianapolis . . .' continued Ferrari. 'Just after the war, I had had occasion, too, to see the 12-cylinder engines of the magnificent Packard automobiles of high ranking US officers.' Thus did the Twin Six tradition take firm and fruitful root in Italy. Packard's last racing entry was a team of special six-cylinder 2-litre cars for Indianapolis in 1923, which proved to be too new and undeveloped to complete the 500 miles

Top: a Packard Single Six tourer 525 of 1927

Centre: a 645 phaeton of 1929

Above: another 645, this being a 1930 tourer now in the Sylvester collection

on the Indianapolis Speedway.

The Speedway entry of a six was significant because Packard's first new post-war model, the first to issue from an expanded and improved plant in 1921, was a six. This was the Single Six, followed to market in June 1923 by the most important Packard of the 1920s, the Single Eight. This replaced the V12, and brought to volume production the classic in-line eight, a type which Duesenberg had pioneered in the US in much smaller numbers. It had, at first, the same bore and stroke as the six, 85.7 × 127 mm, giving the eight a displacement of 5860 cc and an output of 84 bhp, only 6 bhp less than the Twin Six in its final form. It had a cast-iron block with side valves, opened by short rocker levers, mounted on an aluminium crankcase that was fitted with nine main bearings. The otherwise-conventional chassis featured four-wheel brakes with a mechanical linkage, being among the first models from a major American maker to have braked front wheels. A four-speed transmission also came into use on the new Packard eights.

After the business slump of the first years of the 1920s, car sales rose again by the mid-decade, and Packard, now with a new plant behind its spotless reputation, consolidated its position as the number one luxury car in the United States. In 1923, Packard had a slight production lead over Cadillac at the 22,000-car level; in 1926, it built 34,000 cars against Cadillac's 27,489. By the standards of the day, Packard's in-line eight was smoother running than the V8s that were favoured by both Cadillac and Lincoln, and hence kinder to the enclosed bodies that came into use during the '20s. Output kept climbing to the 50,000-car level in 1928, the year when Packard stopped building sixes and placed all its confidence in straight-eights of

north of the city of Detroit during the year 1927.

This proving ground was the womb from which emerged a wider range of Packard cars to meet the challenge of the 1930s. At the top of the range was a completely new 67-degree V12 measuring 87.3 × 101.6 mm for 7292 cc, another Jesse Vincent creation. It had four main bearings and a deep-sided iron block with aluminium heads, and delivered 160 bhp at 3200 rpm. On this new Twin Six chassis, the finest coach-builders of the day, such as Dietrich, LeBaron, Brunn and Rollston, made some of the handsomest cars of all time, automobiles that served as definitions of the 'classic' era in American motor history. However, not many could afford these cars, priced between $4000 and $6000 in those depression years, and only 5744 were made before Twin Six production ended in 1939 not long before the war.

Early in 1932, Packard had introduced another car at the low end of the economic scale, the Light Eight, selling for less than $2000. Although a pretty car, with a unique curved-bottom interpretation of the classic

different bore sizes to suit car weights and price classes. This policy was inaugurated on 1 August 1928 when Packard chose to launch what it called its Sixth Series cars showing, by this designation system used until after World War II, its contempt for the conventional model year changes engaged in by other manufacturers, and at the same time making life difficult for those who would unravel the story of Packard cars.

In those years, Packard came closest to making a sports car, with the Speedster Eight models of the Sixth and Seventh Series. They had large-bore engines with enlarged manifolds, a higher compression ratio and a high-lift camshaft, delivering a sporting 145 bhp at 3200 rpm in 1929–30 trim. Only 220 Speedsters in various body types were built, showing that the type's guaranteed 100 mph top speed held little appeal to the traditional Packard buyer. Special Runabout bodies, built on this chassis by Packard's own custom body shop, were tested for 250 miles at speed by racing driver Tommy Milton at the company's 2.5-mile test track, part of the remarkable proving ground it built on 500 acres

Above: now in the Bruce Cole collection is this superb 833 cabriolet of 1931

Right: a 1934 twelve-cylinder coupé sport in the Du Monte O. Voight collection

Packard grille, the Light Eight failed to catch on and was merged with the main line, simply as the Eight, in 1933. Packard was still the sales leader by a clear margin among the luxury makes (in a shrinking market) when it decided to protect the heart of its range with a completely new car, moderately priced for Packard and in the medium-price range for the industry at large. George T. Christopher was hired from GM to set up the superb new plant to make the car that was announced, in January 1935, as the

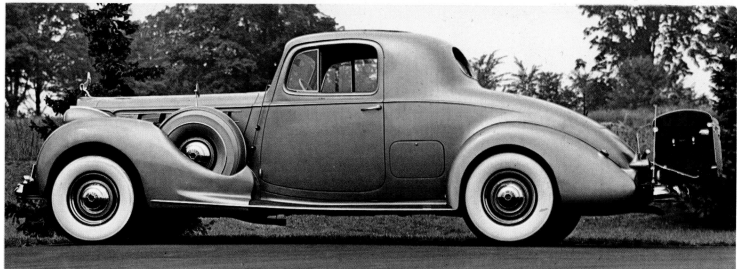

Packard 120. It was named for its 120 inch wheelbase, and was sprung independently at the front wheels for the first time according to a design by research engineer Forest MacFarland. With four-wheel hydraulic brakes, a genuine Packard in-line eight under the proud hood, fresh teardrop-fender styling and a price tag in its cheapest business-coupé form of only $990, the 120 had powerful appeal to the many people who had only dreamed of owning a Packard before. When, two years later, a six was added to the new line,

Top: a 1932 Packard roadster model 900

Centre: a 1938 sport coupé Packard, now in the Conron collection

Above: another 1934 twelve-cylinder car, a coupé roadster

Packard production set the all-time record figure for the year 1937.

Between the 120 and the Twin Six, the straight-eight Packard tradition had been kept alive during the 1930s, against tremendous economic odds, by the Senior Series models carrying 160 and 180 designations. One of the most attractive and memorable bodies built on this chassis was the graceful Convertible Victoria styled by Howard 'Dutch' Darrin for the 1940 and '41 seasons, best known simply as the Packard Darrin, a worthy contemporary of the first Lincoln Continental. The lifetime of the Senior 180 Packard in the West was ended during World War II, when dies for its body and chassis were sold, at modest cost, to the Soviet Union, which had always shown a liking for Packards. Made to cement wartime relationships, this deal accounted for the post-war appearance of Russian ZIS models that looked identical to the pre-war Packard Senior 180 models which had been so successful.

Alvan Macauley made this sale because Packard had introduced a very handsome new body for its Clipper model, unveiled in March 1941, on a 127 inch wheelbase as a competitor to Cadillac in the upper-medium-price class. Its tapering forms were subtle and delicate, flowing back from a high, narrow grille. This was the style with which Packard resumed production after World War II, with both six and eight-cylinder engines. The car was a good one, and the market was ready, but little Packard could not get as much steel as the bigger firms, not even as much as the politically well connected Kaiser-Frazer firm, and production in 1946 was less than one third of the goal of 100,000 cars. In the basis of the existing body, a new shape with full pontoon fenders was styled and introduced as the 1948 model, a husky-looking Packard that sold well in its own country and elsewhere.

Under new direction at the top, George Christopher in 1948 and Hugh Ferry in 1949, Packard's fine engineering staff produced its own automatic transmission, the Ultramatic, highly efficient with a direct-drive clutch in addition to a torque converter. A completely new body style for 1951 was attractive, but

Below left: a 1941 Packard Sedan

Below right: with typical 1940s American styling is this '48 eight-cylinder Clipper

of the car. These excellent new ideas, with an improved Ultramatic and new series names, topped by the Patrician, gave sales new life in 1955—a good year for the whole industry—but they sagged again in 1956, which turned out to be the last year in which genuine original Packard cars were made, due to the Studebaker merger.

The Packard name survived two more model years, 1957 and '58, on facelifted Studebakers, the appearance of which was such that we may be grateful that only 7431 in all were made, including 588 wide-mouthed Packard Hawks in 1958. The last blow fell in 1962 when the Studebaker-Packard Corporation eliminated 'Packard' from its name. Packard, for whom the

Above: the last 'real' Packard was this 1956 Clipper

Right: what would Ralph Nader have said about this 1940 Packard interior, complete with steering column ready to impale!

trailed three years behind the industry pacesetter: General Motors. Under a new head, James Nance in 1952, radical changes were made in Packard, the car and the company. In June 1954, a merger took place between Packard and Studebaker, and three months later the '55 Packard appeared. It was completely reskinned over the lower body, and powered (belatedly) by a new V8 engine offered in two bore sizes to give displacements of 320 and 352 cu in. There was a radical new suspension, too, the invention of William Allison, which used long torsion bars to link the front and rear wheels together to reduce ride pitch and offered also an automatic levelling system for the rear

years between the two great wars were so very successful in every way, never really reached its stride again in the late 1940s and '50s. Unlike other makers, it had not used the 1930s and the war years to build up its own styling and marketing skills, the qualities which, for better or worse, were to spell survival in the Atomic Age. It may not, after all, have been a time in which any Packard car could really have felt at home, so the company's demise may have been for the best.   KL

THE FIRST THING that is noticed about any car is its colour and the condition of its paintwork. The decorative effect may or may not be appreciated, but not everybody realises that the most important function of paint is to protect the body against rust and deterioration caused by the action of the oxygen in the air, aggravated by acid and moist atmospheres.

Modern car manufacturers recognise the need for body protection and go to great lengths to provide it. If the surface of a new vehicle could remain undamaged it would virtually last for ever; unfortunately, bumps and collisions, spatterings of grit and stones and flexings of the body all remove or crack the paintwork. The bare metal is exposed and rust, the great enemy, creeps in, spreading under hitherto sound material.

Production-Line Finish

Rust prevention starts at the steel mill, where newly-manufactured sheet steel is sprayed with oil. During transport to the car manufacturer's body-building line and during the pressing and welding of the many body parts, this film remains and is indeed augmented by additional sealants forced into seams, welding creams, drilling lubricants and similar materials used during assembly. Finally, the completed body shell—a dirty, greasy object—is delivered to the paint shop. The first task is to clean it thoroughly using white spirit and hot detergent pressure sprays. It is then vacuum cleaned to remove every particle of dust and grit, and immediately enters a tunnel on a moving conveyor. In this tunnel, several hundred feet long, paint application areas are interspersed with forced drying sections.

The initial step is to provide basic protection by spraying phosphate etch over the entire body. This material bonds very securely to the metal surface and, when dried, has a slightly rough feel, ideal for keying on the subsequent paint coats.

A paint dip, up to window level, into a bath of red oxide primer follows; after drying, this primer assumes a chocolate colour. Excess 'runs' are rubbed down and then two or three coats of zinc-rich primer are applied by automatic spray. Body sills and other enclosed areas receive applications by long-nosed spray guns through designed-in apertures or holes drilled for the purpose. Each coat is dried and rubbed down, then further sealers are applied along all joints. Next, the underbody seal is sprayed on automatically and the shell is baked to 300°F (149°C) to dry off all traces of moisture.

Two or three coats of acrylic lacquer follow, applied both by hand and automatic spray but with the last coat entirely by hand. The 'high-bake' ovens, operating at a temperature around 240°F (115°C), dry the lacquer coats quickly. Blemishes are removed and then the body is reheated to allow the lacquer to 're-flow'—in effect, this means that a layer of liquid Perspex (Lucite in the USA) forms all over the surface to give a very tough, mirror-like finish.

Finally, the interior voids of the sills are sprayed with a bituminous paint and the finished body is delivered to the assembly line. At every stage, rigid control of paint colour, temperature, viscosity and application pressures has been enforced.

Specialist Repairs

After damage to a vehicle has been rectified, it is handed over to the spray shop to restore its original appearance. The repairman obviously cannot follow the exact methods of a production line since he may be dealing with ten different makes of car in ten different colours every day, each requiring only limited areas of paint renewal. The car may be received by the sprayer

THE FINISHING TOUCH

A paint finish can often mean the difference between a good car and a bad one

with perhaps a new door fitted, or with crumpled areas restored as far as possible.

His first job is to degrease the damaged or renewed areas. Fillers are then applied to bring 'low' patches up to the correct level. When dry, these are sanded down; one or more undercoats are applied followed by further sanding, then two or three finishing coats. These are carefully blended in with the existing paintwork, leaving the appearance of the vehicle as good as new.

This may not sound too difficult, but the professional sprayer has to understand a wide range of materials, appliances and procedures. Some materials react adversely with others, so he must know which are compatible; he must understand colour matching, viscosity and baking, and the handling of his spray guns and other equipment. Many of these procedures can equally well be adopted by the do-it-yourself man and he is advised to do so wherever possible.

Materials

Wax and grease removers: before any filling or painting is commenced, all metal surfaces must be completely free of oil, wax, grease and other residues. White spirit is widely used for this purpose, but there are many other specialised solvents and detergents. It is important not to touch a surface once it has been degreased otherwise 'finger grease' from the sweat glands of the skin will cause contamination and may spoil the adhesion of the paint coats.

Paint removers: modern products will soften old paintwork of any type in 10 to 15 minutes and it can then be scraped off by hand. When stripping glass

Above: a selection of the materials needed in order to make good any blemishes in automobile paintwork. Cellulose primer-surfacer is shown on the left, adjacent to top coat, in brushing and spray-can form; masking tape is useful for covering the areas not to be painted, while the surface should be prepared by rubbing it lightly with wet-or-dry paper. Cellulose thinner is necessary for thinning paint as well as cleaning brushes, and rubbing compound, used when the paint is hard, will produce a deep shine

fibre bodies, the stripper must be removed from the surface after this time otherwise it may soften the basic material.

Rust remover: this is an acidic preparation that not only removes rust, but also reacts chemically with the metal to prevent further rust formation. After application, any sludge formed around beadings and joints should be washed off with water and dried out with compressed air. Filling and priming should follow as soon as the surface is dry.

Fillers, sealers and stoppers: these materials are legion; there are hard-setting fillers that can be forced into joints and cured by heat; there are plastic sealers that will flex with parts of the body; there are rubber and resin-based fillers; there are fillers that can be brushed on, others that can be sprayed and yet others that can be applied by scraper knife. There are also combined primer/fillers which enable two operations to be performed in one action.

Sanding: commonly used grades of 'wet and dry' paper are 180 for the coarsest work, through 230, 280 and 320 for the undercoats, to 400 grade for the finest finish. Except for the coarsest grade, use the paper wet, using long, even strokes, not a circular motion which is almost certain to show through the final coats. Discard the paper before it becomes clogged.

Primers: there are primers available today to meet every need. Chromated primers for maximum corrosion resistance, self-etching primers, red oxide primers and others for use over rubbed down (or 'flatted') paintwork. Always check that the primer used is compatible with the finishing-coat material, otherwise bubbling, streaking or crazing of the final finish may result.

Thinners: most finishes (except aerosols) require thinning before application. Manufacturer's instructions must be followed implicitly in this respect, both as to the type of thinner used and the quantity required to produce the correct viscosity of the finishing paint.

Finishes: the first automobiles were finished with ordinary oil-bound varnish colours, applied by hand but, from about 1920, nitro-cellulose lacquers, which could be sprayed on, came into general use with the development of mass production. High-bake cellulose enamels were developed about ten years later, and were widely adopted in post-war manufacturing plants.

From about 1950 acrylic finishes made their appearance, at first mainly with metallic colours. The acrylic resins used in this material are perhaps better known under the trade name Perspex (Lucite). There are also several synthetic finishes, which do not contain either cellulose or acrylic materials.

The main difference between lacquers and enamels is that lacquer dries out as its solvents evaporate, whereas enamels harden by chemical reaction. The drying of both lacquers and enamels can be speeded up by the application of heat and there are 'high-bake' and 'low-bake' examples of each available. High-bake paints, as we have seen, are used on the body shell on the production line. The repairman cannot use these high temperatures on a completed car or the fittings and trim would be damaged, so he uses 'low-bake' finishes requiring a temperature of around 195–200°F (91–93°C).

As the result of stringent anti-pollution laws, especially in the USA, the discharge of harmful solvents into the atmosphere is being restricted. Research has therefore developed methods of using safe solvents in what are known as non-aqueous dispersion (NAD) acrylics and these are becoming generally available. In the future we are likely to see

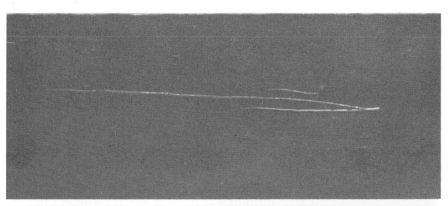

the elimination of all solvents, with paint being applied electrostatically in the form of a powder which is then heated until it flows into a high-gloss finish.

Colour Matching

The professional car-body sprayer must of course be able to match any standard vehicle colour exactly. When it is realised that during the past ten years over 4000 different colours have been employed by car manufacturers, it is clearly impossible for the sprayer to stock each one. Fortunately, the leading paint manufacturers have developed a computer controlled paint matching service to facilitate his task.

Under the scheme, the paint manufacturer obtains a panel of each new colour from the car maker and its colour wave lengths are accurately recorded on a chart by a spectrophotometer.

As a result, the sprayer need hold a stock of only about 40 standard colours from which he can accurately match any body colour, in any quantity, by reference to a printed guide, which gives the exact weight of each standard colour that is to be mixed. An accurate balance, therefore, forms an essential part of the scheme. For example, to prepare British Racing Green, specified weights of the standard colours White, Midchrome, Green-gold, Prussian Blue and Blue-Black are required.

Viscosity

The viscosity of the paint at the moment of application is of the utmost importance and it must be known accurately if a satisfactory finish is to result. Viscosity is measured by timing the period taken by a given quantity of the paint to run through an orifice in a funnel-shaped 'viscosity cup' at a specified ambient

Top: it is very difficult to make good a scratch of this sort, without either rubbing the surrounding area down flush or filling the score. If the scatch has gone through to the bare metal, primer should be applied, but if it is only through the top coat, an application of colour should be sufficient

Above: once the scratch has been levelled, the surrounding area should be masked, using newspaper and masking tape, and the paint applied by aerosol can or spray gun

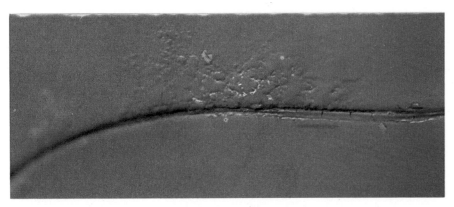

Above: if the paint surface takes on this appearance, it means that water has found its way underneath and caused the metal to corrode; the bubbled paint should be scraped off, then the whole area smoothed with wet-or-dry paper, before repainting commences

temperature. Except when applied by aerosol, the manufacturer's specified viscosity figure for the paint must always be attained, by the addition of thinners, before spraying commences. This figure is quoted in seconds, representing the 'run-out' time of the thinned paint through the viscosity cup.

The effects of incorrect viscosity can be recognised as follows: Paint too thin—surface does not cover and paint 'runs' easily. Paint too thick—coverage is very restricted and paint forms 'blobs'.

Spray Guns

Professional spray guns are operated by compressed air; their purpose is to atomise the paint into a spray and at the same time eject the spray on to the surface being painted. Account must be taken both of the pressure and the volume of the compressed-air supply.

Gravity feed and suction guns with screwed-on containers are commonly used for small areas, but for larger jobs, pressure-feed guns are used; with these the paint is forced up from a container which may hold as much as 45 gallons. There are numerous types of air caps, fluid tips, fluid needles and spreader valves that can be fitted to the guns in order to cope efficiently with various viscosities, flow rates and spray patterns.

The gun must always be held perpendicularly to the surface being sprayed, and each pass must be parallel to the surface (not swung in an arc)—this requires plenty of wrist action. Release the trigger at the end of each pass, otherwise the paint will build up at each end of the stroke and run. If the edges of the sprayed area are masked, start and finish each pass on the masking material.

Before starting any job, test spray an area of any smooth surface such as a piece of hardboard to optimise spray pressure and distance, and to check viscosity. It is usually more satisfactory to spray a complete panel—the whole of a door for example—rather than a small patch. Small differences in colour or texture are disguised if the sprayed area is taken to a natural join in the body.

The correct distance to hold the spray gun from the work is about 8 inches; if held too close, the atomised mist reforms and the paint builds up quickly into a narrow area and runs or sags. If held too far away, the paint droplets are spread out too much and cannot join together. As a result, the undercoat shows through. In addition, if the gun is held too far away, a dusty or sandy finish may result due to excessive volatisation of the thinners between the gun and the sprayed surface. Spray pressure should be set according to the paint manufacturer's recommendations, and may vary between 40–80 lb per sq in (2.8–5.6 kg per sq cm); the finishing coats usually require the higher pressures.

After use, if the same colour will be required again soon, it is sufficient to remove and securely cover the reservoir of the gravity or suction-feed gun. To clean a gun, which should be done as soon as spraying is finished, pass thinners through the gun instead of paint. Wipe the exterior with solvent-soaked rag.

For the d-i-y man, for whom a compressed-air supply is not usually available, the choice lies between the aerosol spray and the electrically operated spray gun. The above notes on the use of the spray gun should be followed where applicable.

Baking

To speed production in the paint-spraying shop, movable booths, drying arches or panels are available. These usually consist of a battery of infra-red lamps and are adequate to provide the low-bake temperatures required. Baking time is usually around 40 minutes.

Brush Painting

Although a brush-painted job cannot really compete with a good spray finish, nevertheless circumstances may sometimes favour brush application, for which special quick-drying cellulose undercoats and lacquers are available. Large areas are the most difficult. For example, a roof, where each stretch, as it is painted, must be joined up to the next before the paint gets too dry. Fast working is therefore called for, with just the right amount on the brush—enough to cover in one pass, but not enough to run. Do not attempt to paint in sunshine, that is, while the metal is hot. Here again, practise on a piece of smooth material first.

After a drying period of at least 48 hours, a fine cutting or finishing compound will produce a good polish. The compound, thinned to a creamy paste with water, is applied evenly with a damp cloth. Take care not to rub through edges or swage lines. Rinse off with clean water and wipe dry.

Cleanliness and safety

For good results, the atmosphere must be dry and dust free. This is recognised by the professional, but the amateur sometimes does not take into account how easily dust can be stirred up merely by walking over a concrete garage floor, how much lint can drop from a pair of cotton overalls or an old pullover, or how much dust can fall from rafters. It is good practice to remove old rags and sacks from the working vicinity, to wash down and dry the garage floor before starting, and to wear nylon overalls while spraying. If possible, support a large polythene sheet over the vehicle, and do the job on a sunny, windless day.

The inhalation of solvents and atomised paint is obviously undesirable and ventilation must be provided. An industrial mask covering nose and mouth should always be worn while spraying. Remember that new paint can take several weeks to harden fully.

Care of paintwork

Most modern finishes require no more than being kept clean by washing: the application of polishes can often do more harm than good. If in doubt, consult the vehicle manufacturer. If the paintwork is damaged, the most important immediate action is to cover any bare metal with paint—an aerosol spray is useful for this job—before rusting can take place. Rectification of the damage can be left until later.

Another often unrecognised source of damage to the paintwork arises from covering the car with tarpaulin or plastic sheeting. This is very bad practice and can cause considerable damage from the sheet flapping in the wind and grinding dirt into the paint surface. In addition, condensation forms under the sheet which is unable to dry out. It is far better to leave the car open to the atmosphere if it cannot be garaged.   GH

THE JET PILOT'S RACING CARS

Airline pilot Hugh Dibley took time out to build racing cars in the late '60s and, although the project stopped for a while, it was later resurrected in 1975

THE MARQUE PALLISER came into being in the late 1960s. Around 150 racing cars, chiefly Formula Fords, were built before the firm became insolvent and disbanded early in 1972. Late in 1974, however, the name was revived by one of the former directors and a new model was announced for the 1975 season.

British racing driver Hugh Palliser Kingsley Dibley was behind the project. The son of a naval officer, and a descendant of Admiral Palliser who served with Nelson, he was born in Hong Kong in April 1937. After entering the Fleet Air Arm for his National Service, Dibley forsook all traces of water for air, and trained as a pilot: he joined BOAC and became an airline pilot. Dibley began motor racing in 1959, at the age of 22, competing in production sports-car races with an AC Aceca-Bristol. He graduated to Formula Junior with Lola cars, and in 1964 raced a Brabham BT8-Climax sports car sponsored by Stirling Moss. He won the supporting race in that year's British Grand Prix, beating Denny Hulme and Roy Salvadori, and also enjoyed success in the United States.

In 1965 and 1966, Dibley raced large-capacity Lola T70s, winning the sports-car race supporting the British Grand Prix once more. The year was 1966 and this time he conquered Chris Amon, Jacky Ickx and many others. In 1967, he co-drove a Ferrari 250LM to a class win in the BOAC 500 at Brands Hatch and was due to race the Howmet TX gas-turbine sports car in the following year's event. However, it was crashed before his turn to race. Dibley also appeared, unsuccessfully, in a Chevrolet Camaro saloon car.

During his racing exploits, Dibley befriended Len Wimhurst, an engineer who worked for Lola and Brabham. Wimhurst cornered Dibley one day in 1966 and suggested he could design and build a car if Dibley would provide the engine and gearbox and race it. The chassis was completed in the backyard of Wimhurst's house in Catford, South London, in December 1966, and by October 1967 the complete car was on the starting grid for its first race at Castle Combe. It was quickest in practice, but retired on the last lap owing to a fuel blockage. At first known as the TBN—to be nominated—the car was eventually christened the Palliser WDB1; Palliser was the second of Dibley's three forenames, W was for Wimhurst, D for Dibley and B for Formula B, a 1600cc production-engine formula popular in the United States, and known as Atlantic in England.

In 1968, Wimhurst built three more Pallisers, again in his backyard, which were sold to customers in the United States for Formula B racing via Bob Winkelmann, the American agent who was soon to become a director of the company alongside Dibley and Wimhurst (the American cars were, in fact, known as Winkelmanns or Winkelmann-Pallisers).

In October 1968, Palliser Racing Design Ltd was formed and Wimhurst moved into new premises in North Street, Clapham, South London. Nearly fifty

cars were built in the cramped, 1700 sq ft premises in 1969, over 40 of them Formula Ford WDF1s and the remainder Formula B WDB2s. Plans for an advanced-specification Formula 5000 car—which was to use side-mounted radiators and other innovations 'borrowed' from the 1968 Chaparral Can-Am car—were shelved owing to lack of time and finance.

In 1970, the bulk of Palliser's production was again shipped to the United States. A works Formula Ford Palliser WDF2 was raced in Britain by Peter Lamplough with encouraging results, while Roger Keele was lent a chassis for Formula Three use. This car, known as the Palliser WD31, was unfortunately plagued with engine problems. Bob Evans, a customer, clinched the

Above: Mike MacDowel competing in the Gurston Hill-Climb of June 1971. His car was based on a Formula B WDH1 Palliser chassis and used a 3-litre Repco-Brabham Formula One engine

Townsend Thoresen Formula Ford Challenge series at Brands Hatch, while Vern Schuppan and Russell Wood also scored successes for the firm at the end of the season. In mid 1970, Palliser took over the production rights of a Formula 5000 project begun earlier in the year by Frank Gardner and Ford designer Len Bailey. Originally known as the Franklen, it was renamed the Palliser-Franklen WDA1. No orders were received for the production of replicas, and the prototype was eventually sold to Australia.

For 1971, a wider market for Palliser cars was sought by Dibley, owing to the poor economic climate in the United States. More workshop space, giving an extra 3000 sq ft, trebled the area available, and the range of cars was increased. Pride of place went to the Formula B Palliser WDB4, a development of the original 1968 car which was now also eligible for the new British category. Basically, it was a multi-tubular space-frame design with stressed panelling, featuring wide-based, unequal-length double-wishbone front suspension and lower wishbones, top links and twin radius rods at the back; it sold for £2400 less engine. Most prolific car off the production line was, of course, the 'bread and butter' Formula Ford WDF3. Of necessity, a more simple space-frame concept, it sold for £1325 less engine or £1650 with a BRM-tuned Ford engine. A high spot for Palliser in Formula Ford in early 1971 came when Peter Hull, later to become McLaren PR man, took Peter Lamplough's works car to South Africa. Hull won the five-race Sunshine Series, sponsored by BOAC and Ford, from Englishman Geddes Yeates and up-and-coming local boy Jody Scheckter. A Formula Three version of the WDB4, the WD32, sold for £2250 less engine (it was virtually the same chassis, but with a Hewland Mk 8 instead of a Hewland FT200 gearbox) and a Formula Super Vee version of the WDF3, the WDV1, was available at £895 in kit form less Volkswagen parts, or £1850 complete with standard 1585 cc Volkswagen engine. The light-alloy monocoque Formula 5000 Palliser-Franklen WDA1 was still listed at £3750, while the range was completed by the Palliser-Daren Mk 3 sports car. Dibley had taken over the manufacturing rights of the Daren 2-litre sports car, designed, built

Right: a Formula Ford Palliser WDF3 in action. A simple space frame design, the car cost £1325 less engine and £1650 when fitted with the BRM-tuned Ford engine. In 1971, New Zealander Peter Hull took one of these cars to South Africa and won the five-race Sunshine Series beating drivers of the calibre of local aces Jody Scheckter and Richard Sterne

ship, driving the works Palliser WDB4 powered by a Ford Twin-Cam engine developed by BRM. It was an excellent achievement, but not enough to save the firm.

Despite initial announcements of an intensive programme to be pursued in 1972, Palliser Racing Design Ltd was offered for sale as a going concern in mid February. Hugh Dibley was now a first officer on BOAC Boeing 747s, and a jumbo-pilot instructor. He could not devote sufficient time or energy to running his firm, which was now in financial difficulties, with few orders on the books for the coming season. Instead of concentrating on making Palliser a profitable company, Dibley had perhaps entertained too many unprofitable deals with customers and had tried to

Above: Irishman Damien Magee piloting his Palliser P742 Formula Ford 2000 to victory at Brands Hatch in early 1975. Although the company producing this model retained the Palliser name it had no business connection with original Palliser founder, Hugh Dibley

and raced by John Green. It had a steel-monocoque centre section and exterior alloy panelling. In addition, a one-off car was built for hill-climb purposes. Based on the Formula B model, this WDH1 chassis was built around the 3-litre Repco-Brabham T740 engine for Mike MacDowel.

Hugh Dibley also revealed that he could construct a Formula Two car for any interested customer, and hinted that in the not-too-distant future, a Formula One Palliser was a distinct possibility.

On the surface, 1971 was a successful year for Palliser with their cars excelling in Formula Ford and Formula B. Vern Schuppan, the Australian driver who at one stage was employed by Palliser to liaise with customers and undertake general administration work, won the Yellow Pages Formula Atlantic Champion-

expand too quickly. He found that race-track successes did not pay the bills.

In mid March, the firm went into liquidation, and later in the year most of the stock was bought by Cambridge Sports Cars, a company run by racing driver Ian Mawby. Lem Wimhurst continued to design and build racing cars, one bearing his own name being campaigned in Formula Atlantic during 1972 Wimhurst revived the Palliser name late in 1974, introducing a car for the new Formula Ford 2000. Known as the Palliser P742 and driven by Northern Ireland driver Damien Magee, it displayed enormous potential and quickly became a leading contender in the 1975 Allied Polymer Group Ford 2000 Championship. A Formula Ford 1600 car, the P741, was also planned. MK

KNOCKING IT INTO SHAPE

Although not a job for the do-it-yourself man, panel beating, the craft, is a very interesting one

THE TERM PANEL BEATING strictly applies to working in sheet metal, using hand tools almost entirely, but today this traditional craft has almost died, as panel beaters have been replaced by sheet metal workers, metal finishers and car-body repairers.

There are, however, a very few limited fields of employment remaining for the panel beater. The main one is in prototype construction for the large motor-vehicle manufacturers and another is in the repair and restoration of vintage and veteran cars. Vehicle repairing on a commercial basis still requires a small but declining number of traditional panel beaters.

The reasons for this decline are economic: panel beating is labour intensive and in the vehicle-repair industry it is far cheaper to strip off a damaged wing and to replace it with a new one (unless the damage is very minor), than to employ a panel beater on time-consuming rectification. Indeed, so complex are some built up welded sections used in car manufacture today, that traditional methods of repair by stretching and shrinking the metal are often impossible.

Fifty years ago, most automobile bodies had wooden frames of beech, oak, or ash. Relatively heavy sheet-metal panels were wrapped around this framework and fastened with nails or screws. As for the metal sheets, simple curves were the rule; curves that could be formed by passing the sheets through rollers. All the parts were assembled on a substantial channel-section chassis.

In the 1930s, heavy press tools started to come into general use. The press tool stamps out a flat sheet of metal into intricate shapes—a door, a bonnet, a facia panel. Today, five-ninths of a typical modern saloon is built up from over 500 different sheet metal pressings, most of which are welded together. Pressings are replacing castings in many instances, and the old, heavy chassis has virtually disappeared. Instead, the

Below: a stepped bar is used in conjunction with a shaped dolly to add the final touches to a Panther De Ville's rear wing

modern mass-produced car is of monocoque construction, that is, a structure in which the body is integral with, and shares the stresses with, the chassis. The monocoque gains its strength from the whole.

Strength and rigidity are given to the sheet metal parts by the curves and angles pressed into the sheets. To understand the reason for this strength, consider a flat piece of sheet which can easily be bent by hand. Now fold up an inch of the sheet at right angles along one edge, and the piece will acquire rigidity in one plane; fold up the opposite edge to make a U shape, or channel, and it is stronger still. Now close across the top of the channel with another sheet lightly welded into place and the square metal section so formed will have attained immense strength for its size and weight. Welded U sections such as these form the main framework of most cars today, the closure to the square section being completed by other components as they are welded into place.

Today there may be one pre-prototype and several prototypes of a car before it enters production; it is in pre-prototype construction that the traditional panel beater can exercise his talents to the full. A new model

usually starts its life as a scaled down replica in clay, which is repeated as a full size model in wood. The panel beater will then have drawings, wooden patterns and the full-size model to enable him to lay out and mark up his metal sheet, form it and test it for fit. Intricate shapes can be made in a number of separate pieces which are welded together on a large steel layout table marked out with the design. For the prototypes, a number of low-cast aluminium or zinc dies, with hardened surfaces, will be prepared from the hand-made components already constructed, so that the hand working is reduced as far as possible.

To understand why some metals can be easily bent, why others are tough or brittle, why some rust yet others are stainless, is to appreciate a vast subject. However, there are some basic properties of metal which the panel beater utilises to his advantage.

The malleability of a metal is its ability to be hammered or pressed permanently out of shape without fracturing. This malleability is the opposite of brittleness—a brittle metal can be fractured with a heavy and sharp blow, but can possess great strength under normal usage. Different metals possess different coefficients of expansion—that is, the amount by which each metal expands under heat or contracts under cold. Bend a flat sheet of steel into a gentle curve and it will spring back; bend it still further and it will crease permanently. This is because it has been stretched beyond its elastic limit; its elasticity can, however, be restored by subsequent treatment.

Differences between steels are caused largely by the addition of varying amounts of different elements in the smelting furnace—a high proportion of carbon will make the steel increasingly brittle and therefore less malleable, for example.

Other differences are caused by the treatment given to metal while it is being worked—if cold metal is

one thickness gauge or measurement system. The British Standard Wire Gauge (SWG)—used for sheet metal also—was legalised in 1894: the Birmingham Gauge in 1914. These two, apart from metric, are the only legal systems in the UK. In the USA, the 'US Government Standard' is used. Therefore, although thicknesses in different gauges are very similar, if an exact match is required it is essential to quote both the gauge number and gauge system.

Aluminium sheets, half-hard grade, are still used in the automobile industry. At one time there were a number of aluminium-bodied vehicles on the market, but sheet steel is stronger and more easily worked into the intricate shapes required, so that this use of aluminium has declined for family cars, although it is still widely used for coaches and vans requiring large, lightweight flat sheets.

The hand tools used include at least seven different types of hammer, of which the most important are the blocking, planishing and the shrinking hammer. The blocking hammer is used for heavy blows, and the planishing hammer for smoothing and final finish. The shrinking hammer is similar in shape to the planishing hammer, but its striking face is coarsely ribbed. The pick hammer has a long curved sharp end for lifting up a dented area. Bumping, dinging and flipper hammers have self-explanatory titles.

Other essential tools include the mallet, left and right-hand panel cutters, snips and an assortment of dolly blocks ('dollies'). These are cast iron or steel blocks with flat or curved surfaces of various radii to match the inside shape of the panel. Their names are descriptive of the job for which they are intended—heel, toe, low crown, beading, wedge, shrinking and button dolly, and the long-reach dolly for double skins.

Dollies are used to hold one side of a panel firmly

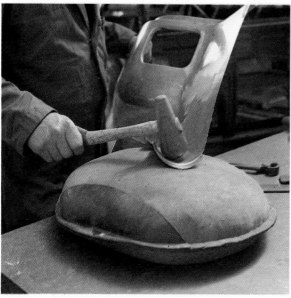

Far left: a leather sandbag is used as a support for some major shaping work with the blocking hammer

Left: a planishing hammer is employed to smooth out a rear light housing

repeatedly hammered or bent in the same place, it becomes work hardened and brittle as stresses are set up. To remove these stresses and make the metal malleable once more, it is heated and allowed to cool slowly. This is called annealing. Steel sheets are available in various grades to suit different applictions: the most useful is cold rolled commercial quality, which has a low carbon content and is highly malleable and has a good finish.

The various thicknesses of sheet steel commonly used in body building can be identified in more than

while the other side is hammered during the process of forming or restoring shape to the workpiece. Then there are flat and curved files for the removal of rough edges and surplus filling. Body spoons have their uses in confined spaces while dog clamps ('dogs') are used to straighten items such as bumper bars and brackets. Other common tools include cold chisels, pliers, hacksaws and punches.

A variety of shapes can be produced in a steel sheet by the use of the wooden shaping block—typically 15 inches square with a 4 or 5 inch hollow, 1 inch deep, scooped out of the end grain. Another tool is the leather sandbag. Both of these are used in conjunction with the blocking hammer.

Even the most versatile of panel beaters will avail himself of the many machines designed to lighten his load and speed production. Such tools include the guillotine, for shearing off metal from the sheet; the folding machine, which will make both rectangular and curved folds of almost any radius, rollers for producing curved panels; swaging machines for raising moulds ('swage lines') along a panel; rotary shears for cutting out irregular shapes; and the burring machine, that will turn up the edge of a panel at right angles.

The wheeling machine—a large and a small-diameter wheel mounted one above the other—is widely used for shaping, for example, a gently curved panel, which is passed to and fro between the wheels, stretching the 'wheeled' area until the required shape is achieved. Foot-operated electric hammers, sanders, pneumatic chisels, stretchers and oxy-acetylene welding plant are among the many appliances available.

Of materials, body solder is widely used to build up sunken areas that cannot be restored, while plastic filler is employed on smaller dents and cracks.

Shaping a new panel may require cutting, shrinking or stretching. For cutting, shears or a guillotine are used. Often, a pattern will first be cut out of thick paper or card, perhaps removing wedges to form a rounded shape, and then used to mark out the metal panel. Corresponding wedges are cut out of the metal, then the edges are drawn together and welded. If only a small wedge shape needs removing, the piece can be shrunk by 'blocking', that is, laying the sheet over the cup-shaped depression in the wooden block already described, and striking one or more heavy blows with the blocking hammer until a crease is formed, running towards the edge of the sheet. This crease is now 'worked out' of the sheet, by lighter hammering. A reverse shape can be attained by forming the crease over a dolly. The panel can be stretched, again imagining a wedge shape, by beating out from the tip of the wedge and gradually increasing the width of the beaten area and the force of the blows up to the panel edge.

When working with aluminium, it must be remembered that it is a much softer material than steel, and less force is therefore required to manipulate it. A smooth wooden mallet and sandbag are therefore the preferred tools to use with aluminium, unnecessary hammering being avoided. Aluminium can be both stretched and shrunk in the same way as sheet steel, but a sander is not used, as it tends to tear the metal away, leaving deep grooves.

With damaged body panels, it is essential to apply correcting forces in a directly opposite direction to the impact that caused them, and to take out ridges and dents in the reverse order to that in which they were made. If this procedure is not strictly adhered to, a well-finished job is virtually impossible.

When a body panel is damaged by impact, the metal is stretched, usually inwards, leaving a depression with more or less well defined non-elastic edges. These edges can be gradually beaten out using a hammer and dolly, but the stretched centre will remain as a bulge, which must now be shrunk.

One method used is to heat the centre of the bulge with an oxy-acetylene burner until it is red hot, then to hammer it causing the bulge to collapse but leaving a wrinkled area. Then, while the metal is still red, the ridges are hammered out with the planishing hammer and dolly—with a smoothing action, towards the

centre—towards which the excess metal gradually shifts in waves.

After the metal has turned black, it is quenched with water, contracting the area still further. This operation may have to be repeated on several spots until the panel is tight. Irregularities are then filled with body solder, or plastic filler, and the area sanded or filed smooth. Another shrinking method is to attack the heated, wrinkled area with a shrinking hammer which forms small ridges, thus contracting the metal. These ridges are then hammered out with the planishing hammer and finished as before.

Both welding and rivetting methods are used to fix panel-beaten steel and aluminium sheets, although special techniques are required for aluminium. For welding, an oxy-acetylene torch is required to join, for example, two butting edges of flat plate, or one channel section to another. If the weld is visible, it must be sanded down, with any pits filled to the same level as the surrounding surface. Electric spot welding is used to join two overlapping surfaces or folded edges.

Rivetting is mainly confined to commercial-vehicle roofs and panels, since the head of the 'pop' rivets mostly used today remain visible. However, the method has its advantages for the do-it-yourself man, since pop-rivet-setting tools can be used in confined spaces and access is needed to only one side of the work. The humble nut and bolt need not, of course, be neglected. GH

Above: the wheeling machine is used for introducing gentle curvature to a panel; the work piece is passed to and fro between one large wheel and one small

THE RECUSANT PIONEERS

Panhard rarely followed design trends, and
for this they were highly respected

THE HISTORY OF THE PARISIAN FIRM of Panhard et
Levassor is a Gallic whole that may be divided into
three parts. The only thing that any of these Caesarian
sections had in common with the other two was a
mild idiosyncrasy, and yet there was an irony in the
relationship of the end to the beginning. The first
period saw the cars of Panhard & Levassor among the
earliest pioneers, although this was not in itself fear-
fully important; and during it, especially in the years
around the turn of the centuries, the cars completely
dominated racing, which was not all that important
either, but they also established the basic format of the
motor car and thus determined, for decades to come,
what was to be the orthodox layout, which may not
have been a good thing but was an extremely important
one. The second phase, which began just before World
War I and lasted until World War II, saw the firm
building some lovely touring cars with sleeve-valve
engines. In the third, beginning in 1945, they changed
their tune completely, building a series of small, light,
efficient and unusual cars that remained in production
for twenty years because they were right, but which
were never made or sold in really large quantities
because the public—conditioned to rely upon the very
orthodoxies that the company abjured—suspected
they were wrong.

Louis-René Panhard was born in Paris in 1841, and
qualified there as an engineer. He then joined the Périn
firm which specialised in making wood-working
machinery, and after a while he encouraged them to
diversify into metal working as well. In 1872, he was
joined there by his friend and former fellow student
Emile Levassor, three years his junior, when he
acquired an interest in the firm which became Périn

Panhard & Cie. In 1886, Périn died, and the pro-
prietorship passed into the hands of Panhard and
Levassor. In that same year, a friend of the latter,
Edouard Sarazin, acquired the Daimler patent rights
for France—but the following year he died, and his
widow later married Levassor. The stage was now set
for the two friends to enter the motorcar industry.

They began by making a car with a V-twin Daimler
engine carried amidships. It ran successfully in 1891,
but the partners were not themselves convinced, and

Below: an 1897 V-twin
Panhard that was
powered by the Daimler
Phönix unit
Bottom: Emille Levassor
drives along in his 1892
V-twin Panhard,
followed by his wife and
some friends in similar
cars

Above: an early Panhard forms the centre of attraction for a crowd at the turn of the century

Near right: another early Panhard, with Surrey top

Far right: an 1891 car now in the Le Mans Museum

after trying rear-engined layouts they finally settled on one that was to become classical: they put the engine at the front with its crankshaft aligned longitudinally with the chassis, the gearbox in line behind it, and thence transmitted the drive to the rear wheels. Originally, the final drive was by a central chain, and the gearbox was not quite what we understand by the term because the gear wheels were actually exposed, not encased. Nevertheless, it was an archetypal gearbox, with which we are still familiar, for it had four forward speeds and a reverse, with an arrangement of mainshaft, layshaft and sliding gears that, with minor alterations, is recognisable in today's cars. It was not so easily managed: the gearchange lever worked through

a quadrant, making it impossible to pass from one speed to any but the adjacent ratios, with an unpredictable neutral lurking somewhere between. It was a device of which Panhard himself said, 'C'est brutal, mais ça marche'. In fact, the whole car was repellent in its crudity: the chassis frame was made of wood, armoured here and there with flitch plates, the tyres were solid, the 'radiator' or heat exchanger for the engine coolant was behind the engine itself, steering was by tiller, and engine ignition by hot tube—although this last complaint should be levelled against Daimler, whose engines were employed under licence. By 1895, the Panhard had at least acquired a float-feed carburettor of Maybach type, in place of the earlier

surface carburettor, but the car was still difficult to control. With solid tyres doing nothing to mollify the ride, the springs had to be very flexible, explaining the choice of the full-elliptic variety; and in the absence of dampers they allowed the car to shake like a jelly, because of the vibrations coming from the unbalanced engine. Even the controls available to the driver were difficult and confusing: there were no fewer than three brakes, in addition to the sprag by which the car might be checked against running backwards downhill. First there was a footbrake working on the transmission, then a handbrake lever which, when pushed, tightened brake bands on the rear hubs and simultaneously disengaged the clutch; and finally a crank handle with a screw jack to force spoon brakes against the rear tyres. To make things even more difficult for the driver, the car was directionally unstable, the steering having no castor action nor any other kind of self-centring effect.

That something so unutterably foul should be so successful in motoring competitions of the *Fin de Siècle* can only be a sorry reflection on the qualities and abilities of the others. A Panhard was awarded joint first place in the 1894 Paris to Rouen trial, tying with a Peugeot. In the following year was held the first real motor race, over 732 miles from Paris to Bordeaux and back, and this was won by Levassor himself who drove

the public—but by then Levassor was dead, as the result of an accident during the race from Paris to Marseille and back. Still the improvements came: aluminium gearbox casings in 1897, pneumatic tyres in 1898, tubular radiators ahead of the engine in 1899 and, by 1900, the classic Panhard format was complete, with final drive by side chains, piano-type pedals and single-quadrant gearchange in place of the double quadrant that had added to the complexities of the original cars. It was evidence of the improvement that was enforced and accelerated by participation in racing, for in the late 1890s the competition scene had been virtually stolen by Panhard. From 1895 to 1900 inclusive, the cars won 15 out of 22 races, the most successful rival being Mors with a score of three. However, when the 20th century began in 1901, the Panhard had passed its prime, and its subsequent decline was due to the firm's apparent inability to keep up with technical progress elsewhere. The 1901 Mercédès designed by Maybach for Daimler-Benz represented an enormous advance in broad concept and detail execution, and it was the cars built in its image—Fiat and Richard Brasier—which were in the ascendant in racing. There were the occasional victories that still fell to Panhard, whose engines grew bigger and bigger in the effort to remain competitive.

This led Panhard to just one more noteworthy innovation. The rules for the Gordon Bennett races (the most important of the early years of the century prior to the inauguration of the Grand Prix in 1906) included a maximum weight prescription of 1000 kilogrammes; and if engines were to be as large as

Above: yet another V-twin Panhard, this one being in the Deutches Museum, Monaco. The car was built in 1895

Above right: one of the first Panhards with a tubular front radiator was this 1899 B1

Right: one of the French Grand Prix team of 1908. The car is a 12,831 cc-powered machine

his Panhard for 48 hours, 48 minutes to average 15 mph. It was not quite a standard production car: this was the year when enclosed gearboxes first appeared, and Levassor doubtless also made good use of the overrider which freed the engine from the restraints of the governor—a system of levers between the camshaft and the valve stem which gave an interrupter effect that normally limited the engine to 750 rpm, at which it delivered somewhat less than four horsepower. This interrupter gear could be adjusted, to alter the maximum engine speed, or entirely inhibited, in which case the crankshaft could spin up to its giddy maximum of 1250 rpm. That year, 1895, also saw the first appearance of wheel steering as an alternative to the tiller, and of the 2.4-litre Daimler Phönix engine that was a twin-cylinder version of the original. The following year came a four-cylinder engine for the racers, to be made available in 1898 to

Panhard (and, to be fair, others) were making them, they needed to be built with a mind for weight saving. It was Panhard who designed engines with forged-steel cylinder barrels and integral heads, each cylinder being bolted separately to the upper deck of the crankcase, with inlet and exhaust ports and sparking-plug bosses welded onto the head of each cylinder and a thin copper water jacket neatly tailored to fit round the cylinder. It was this constructional principle that was adopted for a number of aero-engines in the ensuing years, and was also taken up by Mercédès for the engines of their racing cars—to such good purpose that Daimler-Benz only abandoned the technique

The sleeve-valve system chosen was that patented by Knight, and later developed not only by Panhard but also by Daimler, Minerva, Willys and others. Each cylinder carried a detachable head deeply spigoted into the barrel, the spigot having a circumferential clearance into which the top ends of the two concentric valve sleeves could poke when at the tops of their strokes. Each of the sleeves was reciprocated by a small connecting rod from an auxiliary crankshaft rotating at half engine speed. The crank throws were spaced so that the two sleeves were out of phase by 160°, and with the intake port just below the cylinder-head insert on one side of the engine, and the exhaust

when producing a sports-racing version of their 1955 Grand Prix car.

In everything else, Panhard remained doggedly conservative, and the touring cars suffered just as much as the racers. However, shortly before he died in 1908, Louis-René Panhard retired from the business and handed over its control to his sons Paul and Hippolyte; and it is surely significant that within a year the old wooden chassis frame began to be replaced by pressed-steel frames, that a new monobloc 2.4-litre engine had high-tension magneto ignition, and that by 1910 the quadrant gearchange had been ousted by a gate type such as Mercédès had introduced nine years earlier. 1911 marked an even more significant departure from the firm's previous practice: not only was it the last year in which the two-cylinder engines were made, it was one in which the first production Panhard with a sleeve-valve engine was introduced.

port almost exactly opposite it, the motions of the sleeves uncovered each port in due turn. For relatively large displacement engines run at modest crankshaft rates, this double-sleeve valve gear was very suitable. The performance it yielded was not particularly high, the port sizes being somewhat restricted by the limitations on sleeve movement, but the mechanism was naturally much quieter in operation than poppet valves. Lubrication of the sleeves did present difficulties, which were kept at bay by limiting the engine's operating speeds, but for touring cars of generous engine size such as the range upon which Panhard now embarked, the sleeve-valve engine had a great deal to commend it.

When they resumed normal business in 1919, after the intervention of World War I, Panhard did make some poppet-valved cars, but it was a brief production, finished in 1922. Their main programme was built

Above: the elegant X17 SS coupé de ville Panhard of 1912. This car used a Knight valve system, and is now part of the Automobile Museum in Turin

around the Knight engine, and by the middle 1920s they had improved its performance considerably by the introduction of light steel sleeves in place of cast iron, enabling a longer sleeve travel to be exploited, the outer sleeve being lined with white bearing metal on its inner surface to minimise frictional losses and the danger of seizure. Thereafter, the larger versions of the Panhard could be impressively fast, even though they trailed an oppressive cloud of oil smoke in their wake when driven hard. By 1924, when all models had front-wheel brakes, dynamotor starters, and four-speed gearboxes, the 4.8-litre, four-cylinder Panhard needed little modification before taking the world hour record at 115.3 mph in 1925. Enlarged to 5.3 litres in 1929, the standard car could then exceed 90 mph. A six-cylinder series was begun in 1927, followed shortly by a massive and refined straight-eight, with centralised chassis lubrication, coil ignition and an all-helical constant-mesh gearbox. Of course, not all the cars were big and fast, but they were all smooth and impressive, many of them carrying bodywork of considerable charm and sometimes elegance. The best were very expensive, costing more than the most luxurious Renault of the day, which was no mean car itself in any sense.

Modern design features continued to be introduced, but seldom with such startling effect as was achieved in 1937 when a model known as the Dynamic was introduced. As ever, it had a sleeve-valve engine, a six-cylinder affair in sizes ranging from 2.5 to 3.8 litres. However, with its hydraulic brakes, backbone chassis, worm-gear final drive, and all-round independent suspension by torsion bars, it was almost aggressively up to date in its chassis. As far as the body was concerned, it was more than up to date, it was positively futuristic: the driver sat in the centre, the headlamps were faired in, all four wheels were largely enclosed by

front-wheel-drive exponent, J. A. Grégoire who had been associated in pre-war days with the Tracta. One of his last pre-war designs had been for Hotchkiss, a car known as the Amilcar Compound, with a small four-cylinder engine driving the front wheels, independent suspension all round and a unit construction of body and chassis that was based before integration on a substantial frame and bulkhead structure in aluminium alloy. For his post-war car, Grégoire still concentrated on light weight and independent sus-

deep spats or valances on the mudguards, there were wraparound extensions to the windscreen, triple windscreen wipers, and some extremely bizarre styling. It is possible that the car might eventually have been successful, particularly after its constructors relented and put the driver on the left again in 1939, but war came and such questions had to be left open.

When the war was over, the needs of motorists in general and the French in particular were very different; so were the cars that Panhard set itself to produce in 1945. This marked the beginning of the Dyna series, cars based on a design by the distinguished

pension, still with an aluminium-alloy frame and bulkhead structure, but now with a 600 cc horizontally opposed twin-cylinder engine, air cooled and furnished with overhead valves, capable of a modest 15 bhp and enough to give so light a car tolerable performance. Plans had been made to produce the car in England as the Kendall, and in Australia as the Harknett, but it was Panhard who took it on and developed it. As amended, it had a live rear axle and a four-speed gearbox with an overdrive top, but in general it was entirely in the spirit of the original Grégoire design, with light-alloy bodywork and a commendably high ratio of cabin to overall length. Many of its detail features were to be emulated by others, an example being the wheels which were little more than light-alloy rims bolted to the brake drums. This original car was soon followed by a 750 cc version developing 32

horsepower, and by 1952 there was an 850 cc version as well. Then in 1954 the Dyna became a front-wheel-drive car, with an entirely new body design that many people thought ugly and bulbous but many others recognised as streamlined and capacious and therefore efficient. It was still a light-alloy car in the main, although notable in that no castings were used in the body. It could carry six people at 80 mph, it could average 40 mpg and it was so effective a car that sales doubled, to reach 30,000 in 1957.

One of the least apparent of its features (or perhaps one of the least visible, for it was evident enough by its noise) was the engine, a machine of particularly nice design. It was a flat-twin, but unusual in almost every detail. The cylinders were cast integral with their heads in substantial light alloy with shallow fins, cast-iron liners being pressed into the bores to accommo-

Opposite page, top to bottom: Paul Panhard;

1913 2.6-litre Panhard;

1913 Panhard X 19;

Knight engine as fitted to 1912 X 17 model;

5000 cc Sport SS of 1925

Above left: six-cylinder Panhard two-seater coupé of 1932

Above right: four-door saloon of 1934

Left: the bulky six-cylinder four-door saloon of 1936. Coachwork was by Panoramica

Bottom: the sleek twin-cylinder Panhard CD of 1964 which competed in that year's Le Mans 24-Hour event

date 85 mm pistons of 75 mm stroke, giving a swept volume of 850 cc. The high-domed pistons reciprocated on connecting rods with roller-bearing big ends on a built-up crankshaft, beneath which was a single camshaft communicating with the overhead valves by pushrods and roller-ended tappets. The valves were

streamlined bodywork won the index of performance at Le Mans three years running, from 1950 onwards. Similar streamliners succeeded there in 1953 and again in 1963—and in between there were rally successes which included a class win in the 1954 Monte Carlo event and an outright win in 1961. In

Above: this two-door tourer with its curious flowing lines is the Dynamic coupé of 1938. It is powered by a 2.5-litre engine

Centre right: the futuristic-looking Dynavia coupé was produced by the Panhard company during the early 1940s

Bottom right: also produced in the early 1940s was the Dyna saloon. It was powered by a twin-cylinder 610 cc engine

inclined in hemispherical cylinder heads, but the rest of the valve gear was most unusual and extremely impressive. Instead of conventional coil springs, there were torsion bars to return the valves to their seats: separate forked rockers engaged under the valve-stem collars, pivoted on roller bearings coaxial with a pair of torsion bars. The valve could thus be shorter by a spring length and correspondingly lighter than in conventional designs. The pivot for the rocker which pushed it open was interesting, too, being a spherical bearing that could be moved up and down a threaded pillar to adjust the valve clearance. Later versions were even more refined, the bearing being automatically positioned by oil pressure to give all the virtues of hydraulic zero-lash tappets without the surge, lubrication and corrosion problems endemic in them.

It was a powerful engine: in its milder form it gave 50 bhp at 5750 rpm, but for the very smartly bodied Tigre of 1961 it gave 60 bhp, and even more in the 24 CT and CD sports coupés which were introduced in 1964 and could exceed 100 mph. The Tigre could do over 90, but the 24 CT was more compact and therefore very much more sporting. It was also not a little intimidating: the gearchange was in the worst porridge-stirrer traditions and the handling displayed typical front-wheel-drive characteristics magnified almost to the point of absurdity, with very sharp reactions to variations of throttle in mid-corner. Nevertheless, the basic Dyna Panhard had the makings of a thoroughly effective ultra-light sports-racing car, and many were the specialist designs prepared on the basis of Panhard mechanical elements. Deutsch and Bonnet started as early as 1948, Veritas in 1950, and the very special Monopole Panhard with extravagantly

that year, the regulations had been modified to give smaller-engined cars a chance and, whether by accident or design, the regulations favoured what Panhard had available far more than anything else on the market. The win was therefore dismissed as a matter for controversy, but it cannot be denied that the little Panhard

This page: various views of two and four-door Dyna Panhards. The original Dyna models came into being just after World War II, although the model style illustrated was introduced in the mid 1950s. These large and bulbous cars were powered by small-capacity twin-cylinder engines but were, nevertheless, quite quick. Perhaps the most impressive of them were the 24CT models (pictured at the top and bottom of the page) which had top speeds of over 100 mph, produced from an 850 cc engine

was a very effective car on most kinds of roads, and its outstanding efficiency deserved recognition. Alas, a new ban on cars of less than 1-litre capacity at Le Mans was a bitter blow and, although Deutsch tried to get round this by supercharging the engine (which according to the rules was equivalent to doubling the cylinder displacement) in 1964, the experiment was a failure because the cars retired. They were interesting development machines, with five-speed gearboxes, Girling disc brakes and 70 bhp at their disposal; but the development programme was doomed not to be pursued. In 1965, the Panhard Company was finally integrated with, or swallowed by, the Citroën company which had acquired an interest in Panhard ten years earlier. In 1967, only the coupé versions of the Dyna were made, the 24 CT having disc brakes on all wheels as a memento of that last Le Mans effort, but Citroën needed the factory space, and there were no more. LJKS

THE NEW BREED OF CAT

Some say that 'replicars' are sacrilege, while others love them. Panther West Winds build some of the world's best, and they *are* much loved

TO MAKE A SUBSTANTIAL LIVING from a hobby is an ideal way to live; Robert Jankel, Managing Director of Panther West Winds, achieved just this. He had possessed a great interest in cars from his young days and showed this by working with John Young, boss of Superspeed, and by gaining some notable success on the race track. As an engineer, he was able to design and build his own cars, using various different styles, ranging from vintage to futuristic.

Unfortunately, Bob Jankel found that there was not enough money to be made in the tuning business and he left John Young to enter a new field: the fashion industry. He became Merchandising Director, with a considerable number of shares, of quite a large company, but he did not let this deter him from continuing his hobby and he carried on building cars on a regular basis (about one a year). During this period, friends asked for replicas, and this led to Mr Jankel selling his shares and setting up Panther as a company in 1971.

Initially, the concern was based in the garage belonging to Bob Jankel's Walton-on-Thames home, the office being in the house. The prototype Panther was an elegant vintage-style four-seat tourer, which owed more than a little of its frontal shape to the Rolls-Royce company.

It took only a few months for this prototype to be developed into the first 'production' model, known as the J72 and announced in June 1972. This car was typical of every car to come subsequently from the Panther emporium, in having a hand-made aluminium body, which was trimmed in Connolly hide and gleaming walnut, coated with a massively thick and deeply shiny paint finish and mounted on a sturdy box-section chassis.

The engine for the J72, in its original form, was the Jaguar 3.8-litre XK straight six, and beam axles were fitted front and rear, suspended on coil-spring/damper units. Although not advertised as such, the J72 was built in the image of the SS100 made in the 1930s.

Soon after the J72's introduction, a tuned version, known as the J72S, was launched. Externally, the only difference was that this model had alloy wheels in place of the chrome wire units fitted to be standard car, but the engine produced considerably more power.

At this time, a great deal of the work of building Panthers was being done by outside contractors, but interest in the cars was keen enough to warrant a move to larger premises. Consequently, the company installed itself in the old Cooper Car Company factory at Byfleet, near Weybridge, in Surrey; in the process, Robert Jankel acquired several of the original contractors and incorporated them into the corporate structure. Panther West Winds became responsible for assembly, Panther Shapecraft for the coachwork, Panther Spraycraft for the paintwork, Panther Screencraft for the screen frames, Panther Spincraft for metal spinnings such as hub caps and headlamp bowls and

Panther Trimcraft for the upholstery and trim work.

Several of these subsidiary companies were also performing high-quality work for other companies, including Rolls-Royce, and Panther also offered a design service, all car-design work for the company being executed by Robert Jankel himself.

In 1973, Panther announced two new versions of the J72, powered by either the 4.2-litre XK engine or the new 5.3-litre Jaguar V12. Needless to say, the V12 unit gave the car electrifying performance, although it added about two thousand pounds to the £7500 of the 4.2. Unfortunately, Panther were unable to obtain complete V12s from Jaguar, so they bought sets of 'spare' parts and then assembled the engines themselves. Happily, it was not too long before the company came to more convenient arrangement with Jaguar and purchased complete units.

Minor modifications were made to other parts of the cars when the engine options were changed: for instance, the sidescreens and dashboard were redesigned and the suspension was relocated for greater comfort.

Right: a view of a half-completed De Ville in the Panther West Winds part of the factory. Here, the running gear is added to the complete, painted body

During the first year of J72 production, 45 cars were built for use in nine countries, and this encouraged Bob Jankel to introduce more new models, starting with the Panther Ferrari FF, first seen at the Geneva Show in March 1974.

The FF was based on the chassis and running gear of the Ferrari 330GTC and clothed in a beautiful aluminium body reminiscent of the 1947 Ferrari 125S. As with the J72, the interior was sumptuously trimmed in Wilton carpet, Connolly hide and burr walnut. Remarkably, the design, development and construction of the car were carried out in only three months, plenty of midnight oil being burnt during this period. It was not unusual for the lights of the assembly section

Above: the first Panther, a four-seater tourer, very similar in frontal styling to some vintage Rolls-Royce models

to be on all night whenever a car was wanted urgently.

With their next model, Panther jumped into the future, with a high-class beach buggy known as the Lazer. Announced in July 1974, the Lazer was fitted with the Jaguar V12 engine, giving a top speed of more than 150 mph in the wedge shaped aluminium body. Running gear was also Jaguar and the three-seat-abreast interior was trimmed to the usual high standards. A straight six was offered as an option, but the Lazer was a departure from Panther's more usual style and never became a 'production' model.

Hot on the heels of the Lazer, in time for the Earl's Court Motor Show in October, came what was one of the most expensive cars in the world. With a basic price of £17,650, the De Ville was a real luxury limousine based on the elegant and beautiful lines of the Bugatti Royale, a legendary but disastrous car of the early 1930s. Once again, a Jaguar engine (V12) and Jaguar running gear were mounted on a box-section chassis and covered by a hand-made aluminium body. Unlike the Bugatti, the De Ville had independent suspension all round, together with power-assisted

Above: the 4.2-litre-engined version of the J72, first announced in 1972; this car was loosely based on the SS100 of the 1930s

Left: pride of the Panther fleet, the De Ville; based on Jaguar running gear and styled after the great but unsuccessful Bugatti Royale, this has been one of the most expensive cars in the world

Below: the Panther West Winds workshop, with a line of J72s and a De Ville

disc brakes and wide tyres for safety, while inside electric windows and air conditioning were standard fittings.

The list of optional extras for the De Ville was almost endless, each car, as with other Panther models, being made to 'fit' its prospective owner. Despite the vintage quality of the De Ville and the J72, both were capable of passing the statutory 30 mph crash test, having energy absorbers built into the chassis members where the functional bumper bars were affixed (front only on the J72). In fact, when the J72 was crash tested, it emerged with very little damage.

In 1975, Panther departed from their standard procedure, when they acquired the rights to build the French Monica, designed and developed in England by Chris Lawrence. This was a steel-bodied, four-door, luxury grand tourer, built to compete with the Aston Martin V8 and powered by a Chrysler V8. This move was by way of a rescue bid on Panther's part, as CFPM, who were the French owners, found the car unprofitable and withdrew it from production. As usual, the standard of finish of the car was extremely high and Panther even managed to bring the price down from around £14,000 to around £8,000, a substantial drop.

During 1975, Panther West Winds had various pro-projects on the drawing board, and had even built a Lancia-based version of the Ferrari FF. However, Panther production and design was not concentrated on motoring; the company would undertake any project and see it through from rough sketch to top-quality finished article, although in the case of some of the cars, the construction work was carried out (adjusting the shape until it looked right) before the plans were laid down for subsequent examples.

In April of that year, Mr Jankel was working on the development of a boat to take the world water-speed record for a British customer, as well as on various new motoring projects. Although cars were built only to order, it was possible to obtain delivery of a J72 in two months or so and a De Ville in about six months. The list of owners was very impressive, ranging from royalty and heads of state to stars of the entertainment world. With a 1975 De Ville price of £22,000 (this had been overtaken by the Rolls-Royce Camargue), this was not surprising.   IW

Left: shaping the scuttle panel for a J72

Below: the finishing touches are applied to a De Ville body before it is to be mated to running gear and painted. It is the craftsmanship in areas like this that take up a large proportion of the customer's $60,000

Panther's new offering in 1975 was the
Rio, based on either Triumph Dolomite
or Dolomite Sprint running gear; in
England, it cost up to £9000, depending
on specification. The Dolomite Sprint
used a single-camshaft, four-valve-per-
cylinder engine producing 127 bhp. So,
the Rio Sprint was one of the quickest
and luxurious small cars available

J72

To a great many people, the idea of a replica car is nothing short of sacrilege or heresy.

However, there have been many manufacturers willing to build such vehicles, and many people wishing to buy them. Probably the most famous basis for these 'Replicars' have been the Bugatti 35 and the SS100 Jaguar.

Panther West Winds, of Byfleet, Surrey, are responsible for manufacturing the most accurate and most luxurious replica of the Jaguar, yet the machine that is produced, although very much SS100 in looks, still has a great personality of its own.

Built around either Jaguar XK or V12 engines, the J72 is one of those vehicles that is something of a wonderful compromise, giving one modern roadholding and power with just a taste of vintage heritage built in, to add the icing to the cake.

The XK Panther has the redoubtable 4.2-litre engine, which produces 190 bhp and gives the car a top speed approaching 120 mph, while the 5.3-litre V12 engine, producing 266 bhp, gives the car a top speed nearer to 140 mph. Naturally, the fuel consumption is rather high for both models, working out at 18 and 14 mpg, respectively. Sitting squatly on fat Avon radial tyres, the J72s have remarkably good roadholding, although the ride is of the strictly bone-shaking variety. While the Jaguar engines propel the machines at remarkable velocities, servo-assisted discs all round do their best to stop them.

To finish off the cars' superb aluminium bodies, there is that 'Olde English' combination of walnut-wood dashboard and Connolly hide seats.

ENGINE Front-mounted, water-cooled straight-six or 60° V12. 92.07 mm (3.625 in) bore × 106 mm (4.173 in) stroke = 4235 cc (258.43 cu in) (4.2), or 90 mm (3.54 in) bore × 70 mm (2.76 in) stroke = 5343 cc (326 cu in) (V12). Maximum power 190 bhp at 5000 rpm (4.2), or 266 bhp at 5750 rpm (V12); maximum torque 200 lb ft at 2000 rpm (4.2), or 304 lb ft at 3500 rpm (V12). Cast-iron cylinder block and light-alloy head (4.2), or light-alloy cylinder block and heads (V12). Compression ratio 8:1 (4.2), or 9:1 (V12). 7 main bearings. 2 valves per cylinder operated, direct by twin overhead camshafts (4.2), or by a single overhead camshaft per head (V12). Two SU carburettors (4.2), or 4 Stromberg carburettors (V12).

TRANSMISSION Single-dry-plate clutch and four-speed manual gearbox with overdrive on top as standard. Ratios 1st 3.04, 2nd 1.973, 3rd 1.328, 4th 1, overdrive 4th 0.778, rev 3.49:1. Hypoid-bevel final drive with Salisbury Powr-Lok limited-slip differential.

CHASSIS Rectangular steel ladder.

SUSPENSION Front—non-independent by rigid axle, leading arms, transverse linkage bar, coil springs and telescopic dampers. Rear—non-independent by a live axle, trailing arms, transverse linkage bar coil springs and telescopic dampers.

STEERING Recirculating ball. Turns from lock to lock 2.4.

BRAKES Servo-assisted discs all round.

WHEELS 6 in × 15 in

TYRES E70VR × 15.

DIMENSIONS AND WEIGHT Wheelbase 109 in; track—front and rear 54.50 in; length 160 in; width 65.50 in; height 48.50 in; ground clearance 5 in; dry weight 2576 lb; turning circle between walls 40 ft; fuel tank capacity 28 gals.

BODY Sports roadster two-door, two-seater.

PERFORMANCE Maximum speed approx 120 mph (4.2), or approx 140 mph (V12). Acceleration 0–60 mph 6.6 secs (4.2), or 6.3 secs (V12). Fuel consumption 18 mpg, or 14 mpg.

A man for all occasions

BY 1975, MIKE PARKES had lived in Italy for over a decade. He was involved with various motorsporting projects, but do not imagine that 'Parkesi'—as he was known—was almost an Italian. Nothing could be further from the truth. He remained a polite and charming Englishman —one might almost say a 'typical' Englishman. Photographers crowded around him in the Monza paddock during a practice session for the 1966 Italian Grand Prix, and here was the cool, calm Parkes perched on a wheel of his Ferrari savouring a cup of tea!

Michael Johnson Parkes was born in Richmond, Surrey, on 24 September 1931. His father, John Joseph Parkes, once a test pilot, moved to the midlands in the mid 1940s and was to become chairman and managing director of Alvis. Educated at Haileybury (where Stirling Moss was a fellow pupil), Mike joined the Rootes Group as an apprentice in 1949. He worked for 18 months as a fitter and a further 18 months in the administration department before joining the experimental section, where he was closely concerned with the development of the Hillman Imp, from the design stage in 1956 to its production in 1963.

Mike's first car was a 1933 model MG PB, but it was notoriously unreliable and his father replaced it with a new MG TD on one condition: it was not to be raced. However, Mike did race it—twice—and later went into partnership with fellow Rootes apprentice John Munn to race a 1930 chain-drive Frazer-Nash in vintage meetings. The 'Nash was raced with some success for three years, and in 1956 Mike and another Rootes colleague, Geoff Williamson, jointly purchased a Lotus 11 Club complete with rigid rear axle and 1172 cc side-valve Ford engine. The pair designed and built their own light-alloy overhead-inlet-valve cylinder head (a unit which was commercially produced by Willment), and later the car was raced with the engine supercharged and running on alcohol fuel.

Next, Parkes became involved in the Formula Two Fry-Climax project. This was an advanced, rubber-suspended, semi-monocoque car built by David Fry in collaboration with Alec Issigonis. At that time, Issigonis (designer of the Mini) was working at Alvis and Parkes' father suggested that Mike would make a useful test and development driver. It was a somewhat heavy machine, Parkes having little real success bar a second at Brands Hatch on Boxing Day 1959. Mike was also asked to advise Sir Gawaine Baillie with the preparation of his Lotus 15-Climax sports car, and it transpired that Parkes drove the baronet's Lotus Elite in long-distance sports-car races in 1960. Parkes was impressive, but unlucky, an instance being at Goodwood in the Tourist Trophy where Mike was leading his class when a tyre blew in the closing minutes. In 1960, Parkes also ran a couple of races for Rootes in the works Sunbeam Rapiers and drove a works Gemini Mk 3 in the Boxing Day Brands Hatch Formula Junior race.

In 1961, it all happened for Parkes. He raced for Gemini in Formula Junior and was invited to join Tommy Sopwith's Equipe Endeavour team and race a Jaguar 3.8, a Jaguar E-type and a Ferrari 250 GT. He won race after race and, following his defeat of Stirling Moss at Goodwood on Easter Monday, Parkes was invited to

test a works Ferrari 250 GT at Le Mans during the April test weekend (Parkes was present to oversee the Rootes team's cars). He lapped quicker than the works drivers and was immediately offered a place in the Ferrari team in the 24-hour race itself in June. Driving a 3-litre Ferrari 250 TR61 he finished a strong second to team leaders Phil Hill/Olivier Gendebien. Parkes' total of successes comprised fourteen victories and eight seconds that year, including six wins and six fastest laps in one weekend.

In 1962, Parkes, now 30, was ripe for Formula One. He had offers, but his commitment to Rootes—whose Imp was in its crucial final development stages—led to these being declined. He had a one-off Formula One outing at Mallory Park in a Bowmaker Cooper T53-Climax on Whit Monday, finishing a highly creditable fourth behind John Surtees, Jack Brabham and Graham Hill. His main programme once more comprised saloon and GT racing, while he also enjoyed the occasional works drive for Ferrari in sports cars. He was second in the Nürburgring 1000 km, but at Le Mans a team-mate pushed him off into the sandbank on the first lap. Highlight of the year was the Guards Trophy meeting at Brands Hatch on August Bank Holiday Monday. Parkes won the feature sports-car race in a works Ferrari 246 SP, the GT race in a Ferrari 250 GTO and the saloon event in a Jaguar 3.8—all in atrocious weather conditions against top-line rivals.

Parkes finally left Rootes at the end of 1962, accepting Enzo Ferrari's invitation to go to Italy and become a development engineer/test driver/ works racing driver. Much of his 8 am—7 pm working day was spent either behind the drawing board or testing production-line cars. In 1963, he was third in the Le Mans 24-hours and second in the Tourist Trophy and Coppa Inter-Europa. The following year he won the Sebring 12-hours and the Spa Grand Prix, but later was out of action owing to a testing accident, and in 1965 he won the Monza 1000 km and was second in the Nürburgring 1000 km and Rheims 12-hours. The 1966 season opened well with victory in the Monza 1000 km and more sports-car successes were gained in the Spa 1000 km

Above: best known for his exploits in sports and saloon cars, Michael Parkes has also been seen in F1. Here he drives a Ferrari during the 1966 German GP

and Paris 1000 km. At last he was asked to race a Formula One Ferrari, enjoying second places in the French and Italian Grands Prix.

The 1967 season began with seconds in the Daytona 24-hours, Monza 1000 km and Le Mans 24-hours, but in the Belgian Grand Prix Parkes was involved in a serious first-lap accident. His special Ferrari 312/67 with which he had won the Daily Express Trophy at Silverstone (it had an extended wheelbase so Mike could insert his 6 ft 4 in frame) spun on oil and rolled, throwing out its occupant. Mike's legs were badly broken and if it had not been for immediate attention in the new Grand Prix Medical Unit, amputation would have been likely. Recovery was a long, slow and painful process, but eventually Parkes was back at Ferrari to resume his duties as development engineer. He was determined to continue motor racing as well, and in October 1969 co-drove a Lola T70-Chevrolet in the Paris 1000 km with Dickie Attwood; they were 10th after various problems. Driving an old Ferrari 312P for the North American Racing Team, Mike was fourth in the Daytona 24-hours and sixth in the Sebring 12-hours in 1970. He later raced for the Italian-based Scuderia Filipinetti team for the remainder of 1970 and 1971 in 5-litre Ferrari 512s. Best result was a fourth in the 1970 Nürburgring 1000 km.

In 1971, Parkes quit Ferrari to work for Scuderia Filipinetti, becoming involved with the preparation of a team of racing Fiat 128 Coupés. Later he worked on racing versions of the De Tomaso Pantera, taking time off to race one—and win—at Imola in 1973. In January 1974, the Scuderia Filipinetti having been disbanded owing to the death of its patron Georges Filipinetti, a wealthy Swiss, Parkes moved to Lancia as development engineer in charge of the Lancia Stratos rally-car project. Lancia, like Ferrari, were owned by Fiat, while the Stratos used a 2.4-litre V6 Ferrari engine. It was almost like going home.　　　　　　　　　　　　　　MK

Above: Mike Parkes in action in the Ferrari 250TR61 of 1961. This was the first year that Parkes drove for Ferrari and his drive came about in unusual circumstances. While overseeing the works Rootes team at the Le Mans test day in April 1961, he was approached by Ferrari and invited to test drive one of their machines. Parkes, casually dressed in sports jacket and grey flannels, sauntered down the pit apron, climbed into one of the works Ferraris and within a short space of time was proving faster than any of the works drivers who included Mairesse, Hill and Gendebien. Consequently, Parkes was offered a full works drive and found himself driving in the 1961 Le Mans event in the latest 250TR61 Ferrari sports/racing machine. Co-driving with Willy Mairesse, he finished second in the event. He continued to drive for Ferrari and finished the season with fourteen wins and eight second places to his credit. The following season saw Parkes make his Formula One début in a Cooper but it was not until 1966 that Ferrari included him in their Formula One team. The Italian firm found it necessary to build a special long-wheelbase machine to the 6 foot 4 inch frame of the driver, but by all accounts the extra effort was worth the trouble.

THE RACES THAT STARTED IT ALL

Motor racing as we know it today is a far cry from the pioneer days of the Paris races.
Nevertheless, the sport owes its origins to these marathons of endurance and cunning

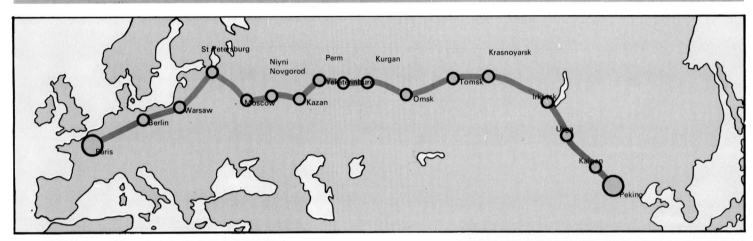

Above: a map showing the route the marathon men took from Peking to Paris. Although this was not one of the 'Paris' races, it nevertheless caused quite a stir. Five cars started on the trip in 1908, organised by *Le Matin*. They left Peking on 10 June at 8.30 am, and the winner arrived in Paris on 10 August after waiting at nearby Meaux for a reception to be prepared. Three other cars finished the course three weeks later and the fourth car broke down 10 miles from the start!

Left: the Levassor monument at the Bois de Boulogne

Right: the winning Itala of the Peking–Paris race

TO THE WEST OF PARIS, in the middle of the confusion of roadworks where the Boulevard Peripherique slices across the tip of the Bois de Boulogne, at the Porte Maillot, is a little public park, a haven of green between the concrete. Its focal point is a grandiose monument, rearing skyward like a cyclopean tombstone, which bears across its pediment the simple inscription 'A Levassor', and depicts, in vivid bas-

relief, the epic drive of Emile Levassor in the 1895 Paris–Bordeaux–Paris race, 'the keen-faced man gripping his steering lever, bending over his car as he passes the cheering crowds'. It is an apt memento of those days when Paris was the focal point for marathon motor races across the dusty miles of the public highways which linked the major cities of the Continent.

As early as 1887, the *Velocipede* journal had attempted to organise an automobile race on the outskirts of Paris, but received only one entry, a little steam quadricycle driven by the Comte de Dion, which trundled solemnly down the short course before being declared the winner of the race. In 1894, Pierre Giffard, editor of *Le Petit Journal*, organised a reliability trial for horseless carriages on the road from Paris to Rouen, but this was just a test of reliability and economy of operation, with no official notice taken of the speeds or times of arrival of the competing vehicles, so cannot be considered as a race.

Not unnaturally, the keener motorists thought this a rather tame enterprise and, led by the Comte de Dion and the Baron de Zuylen de Nyvelt de Haar, pressed for a proper race over a more realistic distance—

seating more than two people would be eligible for the premier award of 50 per cent of the prize money. However, their defence was that they were not encouraging sheer speed, but a combination of speed and reliability, and that cars which were merely fast could not win, for they were bound to break down. As cars with only two seats were obviously designed for speed, *ergo* they could not win outright. Makers could not enter several cars of identical design, drivers were allowed to be changed *en route*, and repairs could only be made under official observation using parts carried in the cars.

Nearly £2800 in prize money was subscribed, by such notable motoring enthusiasts as James Gordon Bennett and William Kissem Vanderbilt, and a total of 46 vehicles was entered, 23 of which were petrol-driven, 13 were steam-powered, two were electric and the remainder were tricycles and bicycles of various sorts. These were remarkably unimpressive in the race, and M. Collin, who made out the official report for the French Institute of Civil Engineers, concluded that the motor bicycle would never be anything other than a curiosity, and that even single-seater vehicles would always need to have four wheels.

Car makers laid their plans for the race carefully: Panhard and Levassor arranged reserve drivers at Ruffec, the halfway stage, so that their cars each had only two drivers throughout the race (supply points were arranged at Orléans, Chatellerault, Ruffec and Bordeaux), while Peugeot gave their drivers special

perhaps as much as 700 miles. Pierre Giffard was willing to organise such a contest, but his board of directors forbade such a project out of hand: 'No one could cavil at a competition in which reliability was the chief factor; but a long race in which speed was the be-all and end-all was quite another thing. Supposing an accident were to take place—and if these automobiles could really attain the terrifying speed of fifteen or twenty miles an hour on the ordinary road, as had been proved in Paris–Rouen, such a catastrophe was more than likely to happen—it would give a handle to the political opponents of the *Petit Journal* which could be used with disastrous effect.'

Undeterred by these voices of gloom, De Dion organised a committee to administer the proposed race. This committee, which first met at De Dion's house on 2 November 1894, subsequently formed the nucleus of the Automobile Club de France. In mid-December, the committee issued regulations governing a 732-mile race from Paris to Bordeaux and back, to take place the following summer.

It was immediately apparent that the committee was playing safe, for they stipulated that only cars

Top: the winning Itala of the Peking–Paris race now housed in the Automobile Museum, Turin

Above: some of the problems faced by the Peking–Paris competitors

route instructions which included railway timetables in case of breakdown. As it happened, these two marques were the principle contenders for the prize money, the Panhards gaining a considerable advantage from their front-mounted engines—not from any consideration of weight distribution, but simply because the wind blew out the ignition burners on the rear-engined Peugeots.

Emile Levassor, driving a two-seater Panhard, went into the lead after Vouvray, driving through the night by the fitful gleam of his oil lamps at such a speed that his relief driver was still asleep when he reached Ruffec. So Levassor drove on, three hours ahead of the rest of the field, and turned round at Bordeaux with no more refreshment than (according to one story) champagne or (another version) *bouillon*.

Levassor entered Paris just before 1 pm on Thursday 13 June, having taken 48 hours 48 minutes to cover the distance, an average of 15 mph. He was six and a half hours ahead of the next car, Rigoulot's Peugeot, but Levassor had not won the main-prize, for his car was only a two-seater. His, however, was the moral victory and, as Rigoulet's car was also a two-seater,

the first prize of 31,500 francs went to the third car on elapsed time. This was Koechlin's Peugeot, which took 59 hours 48 minutes and arrived just before midnight, along with Doriot's Peugeot, by which time the waiting spectators can hardly have been con-consumed with excitement. There were another five hours to wait for the next car, a Roger-Benz, and the remainder of the survivors straggled in over the next 30 hours, the ninth and last (and only remaining steam vehicle), an 1880 Bollée, limping home at 6 am on the Saturday morning, having averaged 6 mph for the race.

The big race of 1896 was the Paris–Marseilles–Paris run over ten daily stages to eliminate strain on the drivers, but a change of date from October to September to avoid clashing with the Czar's state visit to Paris introduced a fateful element that was to turn the race into a gruelling tragi-comedy for the drivers.

After the first day's racing, the weather changed unexpectedly and dramatically: the barometer dropped like a runaway lift and a freak storm swept across the country. The wind uprooted trees and telegraph poles, and torrential rain transformed the roads into slippery quagmires. Competing cars were blown across the road by a near-hurricane wind, which was powerful enough to stop them dead when it hit them head on; it also played havoc with the ignition burners of the engines.

Amédée Bollée ran full tilt into a tree blown down across the road, shortening the wheelbase of his car by several inches and hurling his passengers into the mud; Delahaye's path was also blocked by a fallen tree, and he had to borrow a saw from a nearby cottage to cut the trunk into three and drag away the middle portion to clear his route. Bollée's car, No 21, was charged by a maddened bull and damaged beyond immediate repair; Panhard No 7 overturned and broke a wheel after colliding with a cart (but was repaired) and the crew of the Rossel, having pushed their car up a steep hill, sat down for a breather only to see the vehicle, set in motion by a sudden gust of wind, run away back-wards and smash to flinders at the foot of the slope.

Near Orange, the leading car, Levassor's Panhard, hit a dog and rolled over (always a likely occurrence with those stubby, high-built cars with their sensitive *queue de vache* tiller steering), inflicting internal injuries on Levassor which prevented him from driving after Avignon and which hastened his prema-ture death the following year.

On the way home, Panhard No 7 hit another cart and called it a day, while the Rochet-Schneider was attacked by another mad bull and badly damaged. The winner was Mayade's 8 hp Panhard, whose average speed of 15.7 mph was highly creditable under the circumstances; no less remarkable was the fourth place

More problems for the men on their way to Paris. Luckily, though, there are plenty of locals ready to get them out of trouble

secured by the injured Levassor and his co-driver, d'Hostingue, at an average speed of 14.8 mph.

There was no great race during 1897, just a 106-mile contest from Paris to Dieppe, remarkable more for technical innovations such as the extensive use of aluminium on the Panhards of De Knyff, Hourgières and Prévost, and the introduction of the Grouvel & Arquembourg gilled-tube radiator on Girardot's Pan-hard: racing really was beginning to improve the breed!

The other Paris-based race of 1897, Paris–Trouville, was of similar length. The first four Panhards to arrive all had the new gilled-tube radiators, while ex-racing cyclist Charron had endowed the boxy prow of his Panhard with a 'wind-cutting' fairing which seemed to give him no extra speed at all, as he finished twelfth. The most powerful machine in the race was de Dion's

Top: Giraud with the 12 hp Panhard on the Paris–Berlin of 1901

Above: a Peugeot on the first ever race, the Paris–Rouen. The car is a 954 cc V-twin seen at the Peugeot works in Valentigney

27.0 mph: speeds that were quite remarkable in their day.

In 1899, there were several races centred on Paris: the Paris–Bordeaux, run in a single day and won by Charron's Panhard; Paris–Roubaix, restricted to motor tricycles; Paris–St Malo, which attracted 92 entries, mostly tricycles; Paris–Trouville, a curious handicap event between cars, motor cycles, bicycles, horses and pedestrians, in which the order of arrival was horse, horse, motor cycle, car! Then there were Paris–Ostend (won by Girardot's Panhard), Paris–Boulogne (another victory for Girardot, belying his nickname of 'the eternal second') and the main race of of the year, the Tour de France. This 1378-mile marathon started and finished at Paris, and saw the début of the remarkable Bollée *Torpilleurs de route*, which had such advanced features as independent front suspension, a steel-channel chassis underslung at the rear and a four-cylinder engine (the first successful monobloc unit) mounted at the rear of the chassis. Alas, the carburettors sucked in road-dust and spoiled the new car's chances, their best showing being fifth place behind four Panhards.

The main race of 1900 was the Gordon-Bennett, but the Paris–Toulouse–Paris seems to have been better sport. It had started as part of an over-ambitious event called the *Course du Trèfle*, which was then replanned as *L'Etoile*, a series of races starting and finishing in Paris, which was dropped in favour of *L'Eventail*, a series of races starting in Paris with a variety of finishing points. This too, proved impossible to organise, and the final result was the 837-mile Paris–Toulouse–Paris race, which saw the first-ever entry of an English-built racing car in an international event. The car was the 16 hp Napier driven by S. F. Edge (which failed to finish); the race was won by the consumptive 'Levegh' (the *nom de course* of one Velghe) driving a Mors—it was the end of Panhard invincibility.

As the 1900 Gordon Bennett had been such a shambles, the 1901 event was combined with the Paris–Bordeaux and proved an even bigger flop, as the only Gordon Bennett entrant to finish was Girardot, who was ninth in the open race, which was won by Fournier's Mors. The second car home in the light-car category was Baras's Darracq, which arrived at Bordeaux with the engine held in the chassis by rope, as the bearers had broken!

The great race of 1901, the Paris–Berlin, was the last major event organised under a total formula libre, with no restrictions on engine capacity or overall weight. Its main hazard was the lack of crowd control in the villages through which the course passed, which resulted in a number of accidents—Pinson went one better, and avoided the crowd but wrapped his 40 hp

tricycle, a flimsy affair with a monstrous 18 hp engine grafted on behind.

The year 1898 saw the *Criterium des Entraineurs* from Paris to Bordeaux, notable mainly as the first race in which racing colours were used, the Panhards of De Knyff, Charron and Girardot being painted blue, white and red respectively, and the spectacular Paris–Amsterdam–Paris race, designed as a demonstration and race combined, to prove to the world at large the capabilities and use of the self-propelled vehicle, which was still regarded in many places as an invention of the devil, and was thus divided into 'racing' and 'touring' classes.

An element of farce was introduced by M. Bochet, examining engineer to the Prefect of Police of Paris, who unexpectedly insisted that all the cars should possess roadworthiness certificates, which were required under an obsolete law. The worthy Bochet then examined—and failed—most of the competitors, and refused to allow permission for the race to start. To prevent anyone from starting without authority, Bochet posted a squadron of infantry on the Joinville road, then rode out to the official starting point at Champigny with a half-squadron of Hussars, having placed two guns on the road to Bry, so that any 'rebellious automobilists' could be mown down! The problem was solved by moving the start into the neighbouring Seine-et-Oise area, where M. Bochet had no power of jurisdiction! This race saw the first real challenge to the Panhards in the shape of the new Bollée 'torpedoes', one of which, driven by Etienne Giraud, came third, behind Charron and Girardot's Panhards, all three cars beating the special Paris–Amsterdam train at speeds averaging between 26.9 and

Panhard around a tram in a German town. The other hazards were stray dogs and choking clouds of road-dust, which obscured all forward vision—Degrais (Mercédès) thought he had the answer to this in steering by the treetops above the dustcloud, until he reached a point where the trees marched straight on and the road turned sharp left, with expensive consequences for the Mercédès!

The winner was Fournier's Mors, which averaged 44.1 mph over the difficult 687-mile course, having led most of the way, and thus kept ahead of the dust.

The 1902 Paris–Vienna saw competing vehicles limited to a maximum weight of 1000 kg (plus an allowance of 7 kg for a magneto), which had the unfortunate effect that manufacturers attempted to gain the maximum power-to-weight ratio by cramming huge engines into flimsy frames. Typical were the Panhards, with 13,672 cc engines in armoured wood chassis. After necessary frame reinforcement, the Panhards proved robust enough to take first, third, fourth and fifth places in the heavy-car class (the unbraced frame of Jarrott's sister car, which was 23rd overall, broke *en route* and was patched with string and wood from a bedside table, smuggled out of an hotel in the driver's trousers). It was not a walkover for the monstrous Panhards though, for the first car home was the little 16 hp, 5429 cc, Renault driven by Marcel Renault. The Gordon Bennet had been combined with this race, and was won by Edge's 40 hp Napier, which came 15th in the general classification.

The route control of the Paris–Vienna had been carefully organised, with flag-waving marshals at every dangerous bend, but the lessons of that event were not applied to the great race of 1903, the Paris–Madrid, which was organised against a background of French Government disapproval (although King Alfonso had readily given permission for the Spanish part of the event).

The decision was taken to start the race at 3.30 am on the morning of Sunday 24 May, so that the maximum number of spectators could watch the cars pass through France. The competing vehicles represented the zenith of the misguided attempts of designers to subordinate all considerations to sheer engine power, their attempts at lightening their chassis often overruling all considerations of safety and strength.

The racers were given a triumphant send-off from start at Versailles; a crowd of 100,000 people streamed out of Paris in the night. Along the route were countless cyclists with Chinese lanterns slung from their handlebars, wagonettes, omnibuses, carriages, touring cars, with the occasional racing car, with open exhaust and raucous siren, forcing a path through the throng.

At 3.45 am, Charles Jarrott led the field away down the road to Bordeaux, the dense crowd just parting sufficiently to allow the cars to pass: 'It seemed impossible that my swaying, bounding car could miss the reckless spectators', he later recalled. 'A wedge-shaped space opened out in the crowd as I approached, and so fine was the calculation made that at times it seemed impossible for the car not to overtake the apex of the human triangle and deal death and destruction. I tried slowing down, but quickly realised that the danger was as great at 40 miles an hour as at 80. It merely meant that the crowd waited a longer time in the road; and the remembrance of those hundreds of cars behind me, the realisation that the hunt had commenced, made me put on top speed, and hope that Providence would be kind to the weak intellects which allowed their possessors to run such risks so callously.'

Needless to say, there were fearful accidents. The day was swelteringly hot, the road was exceedingly

dusty, and the *Services d'Ordre*, who were supposed to be keeping the crowds back, 'served . . . merely as additional crowds, specially privileged to stand in the middle of the road at all danger points. The result was a double line of human hedges scarcely two metres apart, between which one was asked to race at upwards of 80 mph.'

The carnage of Paris–Madrid has become legendary: 'all the later starters had passed cars in various stages of collapse—some in ditches, some in fields, some mere tangled and smoking heaps of scrap iron'. Marcel Renault had overturned with fatal results, Lorraine Barrow had hit a tree at 80 mph with a dog jamming the steering of his De Diétrich, Stead had been crushed when his sister car had overturned after an 80 mph collision with another competitor and Porter's Wolseley had burst into flames, killing Porter's mechanic, after hitting a wall in an attempt to avoid a closed level-crossing gate which had been deserted by its signalmen. Gras (De Diétrich) had hit another level-crossing gate, Beconnais (Darracq) and Jeandre (Mors) had run into one another and Tourand (Brouhot) had gone into the crowd in an effort to miss a soldier who had dashed after a child which had run into the road—the child, the soldier and Tourand's mechanic were all killed.

The 'Race to Death', as it was known, was halted at Bordeaux by Government edict, and the surviving cars were hauled to the railway station by draught horses, ready to be shipped back to Paris by train. It was one of the unpleasant episodes in the entire history of motor racing and one which caused much sorrow.

The first man home at Bordeaux was Gabriel, driving one of the new Mors Dauphines, with a streamlined 'upturned-boat' bonnet, who, starting 168th, had carved his way through the field, through the scores of cars, blinding dust-clouds and wrecks, in 5 hours 14 minutes running time, averaging over 65 miles an hour.

After Paris–Madrid, the great age of the city-to-city races was over. Let Charles Jarrott add the post-script: 'To my mind, it was a fitting end to an inevitable happening that the curtain should have been rung down on the Paris–Bordeaux road, the scene of many a Titanic struggle, and the road on which Levassor himself showed to the world at large, in the first great motor race in history, the vast and far-reaching possibilities of the motor-propelled vehicle.' DBW

Above: Henri Farman takes time out to have a word with his riding mechanic on his way, with 80 hp Panhard, on the Paris–Vienna 1902 event. He is pictured in between Vienna and Salzberg, and later finished the race in second place

REG PARNELL WAS Britain's top Grand Prix driver in the immediate post-war years. He began as a wild, seemingly reckless driver in the mid 1930s, but after World War II his style had matured. Parnell raced successfully into the mid 1950s and then became a team manager. His vast experience and knack of spotting up-and-coming drivers paid dividends and 'Uncle Reg', as he was affectionately known, was sorely missed when he died in January 1964.

Born in Derby in 1911, Parnell was introduced to motoring at the age of 15. Although two years under age, he drove his family's lorries and private buses, and in his spare time he performed odd jobs around the garage. In 1934, Reg spectated at Donington Park in Derbyshire and immediately decided to try racing for himself. For £25, he bought an old 2-litre Bugatti single-seater, but it broke its back axle in the paddock at its first meeting. Owing to the expense of purchasing spares for the 'Bug', it was sold and an MG Magnette K3 purchased. The MG was extensively modified—it had a centralised single-seater body, Lancia independent front suspension, a twin-cam McEvoy cylinder head, a two-stage Zoller supercharger and two-leading-shoe Lockheed hydraulic brakes. Wins were secured at Brooklands and Donington Park until an incident on the Brooklands banking during practice for the 500-mile race in 1937. Parnell slid into Kay Petre's Austin and, although Petre was seriously injured and she put the incident down to 'bad luck', the RAC revoked Parnell's racing licence for two years (he was not popular with everyone owing to his press-on-regardless driving style and his admission that, although he loved its thrills, he went motor racing primarily to win money).

His licence was restored in 1939 and Parnell was back with a 4.9-litre Bugatti-engined single-seater known as the BHW, with which he was particularly successful at Donington Park. He also began the construction of his own car for voiturette racing (the pre-war version of Formula Two). Known as the Challenger, it was to feature a specially constructed, twin-stage supercharged, six-cylinder, 1½-litre engine, double-wishbone front suspension, and torsion bars coupled with a de Dion axle at the rear; however, World War II intervened. Parnell spent the war years completing the Challenger (but using a straight-eight Delage engine in place of the partially completed, home-brewed six) and building up a comprehensive collection of racing machinery. This included Alfa Romeo, Riley, ERA, Delage, MG and Maserati models.

In 1946, with motor racing resuming, Parnell owned and raced a Maserati 4CL, an ERA A-type and several Rileys and Delages. The Challenger was, however, sold. It was a year of poor mechanical reliability, although his Maserati was second to 'B. Bira's' ERA in the Ulster Trophy at Dundrod by a mere second. In 1947, as Britain's most successful driver, Parnell won the BRDC's Gold Star. He began that year by winning two ice races in Sweden with his ERA A-type and later won the Jersey Road Race in the Maserati. He acquired one of the ERA E-types and, but for a broken de Dion tube, would have won at Ulster. The following year Parnell again won the BRDC Gold Star. He was third with the Maserati in the inaugural Zandvoort meeting in Holland and with a new Maserati 4CLT/48 (which replaced the luckless ERA E-type) he finished fifth in the Italian Grand Prix. He won the Goodwood Trophy at the first-ever race meeting at the Sussex track and was second at Penya Rhin in Spain.

In 1949, Parnell maintained his winning ways with the Maserati, gaining many successes at Goodwood (he became known as Emperor of Goodwood) and raced at almost every circuit in Europe; he also drove in the early-season South American races. The following season Reg received a tremendous accolade. He was invited to drive the fourth works Alfa Romeo 158 in the European Grand Prix at Silverstone and finished third. Later in the year, he was signed to drive for the Aston Martin sports-car team, taking a DB2 to first place (fourth overall)

Below: Reg Parnell driving the raucous BRM V16. After a successful career as a driver he turned his attention to the tasks of team management

Pressing on for Britain

in the 3-litre class of the Tourist Trophy at Dundrod. He also gave the BRM P15 V16 Grand Prix car its best ever initial results, winning two short races at Goodwood at the end of 1950 and placing fifth in the 1951 British Grand Prix, despite being almost roasted alive in the cockpit.

Above: Reg Parnell in action in his own privately entered Ferrari single-seater machine. Parnell made his name during the early 1950s because of his courageous and tenacious driving of Tony Vandervell's Ferrari-based Thinwall Specials. His driving career ended in 1957, however, with his retirement. Soon afterwards, he was appointed team manager of the works Aston Martin team. His vast racing experience was to transform the team. By 1969, the team had won the prestigious Le Mans 24-hour event plus the World Sports Car Championship. He was also a prodigious talent spotter and promoted, among others, Jim Clark and John Surtees—future world champions both. Following Aston Martin's withdrawal from racing in 1970, Parnell moved to the Yeoman Credit (later Bowmaker) Formula One team. When this in turn folded he became a private entrant supplying cars to the talented youngsters Chris Amon and Mike Hailwood

Perhaps one of Reg's greatest drives was in the 1951 *Daily Express* Trophy race at Silverstone. Driving Tony Vandervell's modified Formula One Ferrari 375 (known as the Thin Wall Special) he left the star-studded field standing in conditions so bad the race had to be stopped after 11 laps due to flooding. He was second to Farina's Alfa Romeo at Dundrod and Goodwood and won at Winfield in Scotland. In 1952, he enjoyed class wins at Silverstone and Boreham driving for Aston Martin; at Goodwood he unhesitatingly took over duties as team manager for Aston Martin when a pit fire seriously injured John Wyer. For Parnell, it was a foretaste of things to come. The 1953 season was a particularly successful one: Parnell was fifth in the Mille Miglia (driving on the ignition switch after a broken throttle had to be wired up in the fully-open position), second in the Sebring 12-hours, first in the Goodwood 9-hours and second in the Tourist Trophy, each time driving for Aston Martin.

In 1954, in addition to his Aston Martin commitments, Parnell drove his own Ferrari 625 in Formula One events, winning at Goodwood, Snetterton and Crystal Palace. Next season he secured more victories for Aston Martin (at

Above: Reg Parnell wrestling the wheel of Tony Vandervell's Ferrari-based Thin Wall Special. Parnell was one of Britain's top post-war drivers

Silverstone, Oulton Park and Charterhall), but in 1956, following an unsuccessful sortie to New Zealand with an experimental single-seater Aston Martin, Parnell crashed Rob Walker's Formula One Connaught B-type at Crystal Palace on Whit Monday, suffering a broken collar-bone and a badly cut knee. He recovered and took his Ferrari to New Zealand, winning the New Zealand Grand Prix and the Dunedin Trophy, early in 1957.

Then came the news: Reg Parnell, at the age of 45, was to retire from active motor racing. He was appointed team manager to Aston Martin and performed his new duties well. After seven years as a team driver, it was no 'sympathy' job. Parnell was able to use his enormous experience to the full and had the knack of picking out future top drivers. In addition to overseeing Aston Martin's World Sports Car Championship season of 1969—the year the marque also won the Le Mans 24-hour race, after many seasons of trying —he encouraged such newcomers as John

Surtees (the motor-cycle World Champion) and Jim Clark.

When Aston Martin withdrew from racing at the end of 1960, Parnell moved to Yeoman Credit (later Bowmaker) who sponsored a Formula One team. His drivers were John Surtees and ex-Aston man Roy Salvadori. When Bowmaker withdrew at the end of 1962, Parnell opted to continue as a privateer, purchasing the ex-Bowmaker cars and the premises at Hounslow, Middlesex. After a visit to the early-season New Zealand and Australian races in 1963, Parnell signed 19-year-old New Zealander Chris Amon to lead the team and also gave encouragement to motor cyclist Mike Hailwood.

For 1964, Parnell commissioned Les Redmond to design a new car to supplement and eventually replace the ex-works, BRM-engined Formula One Lotus 25s he had purchased for the season. However, following an operation, Parnell died on 7 January. Only 53, the seemingly indestructable, ever-smiling Parnell was gone. R. H. H. 'Tim' Parnell, his son, took over control. Tim Parnell finally disbanded the team in 1970 when he was given the job as team manager to BRM; at the end of 1974, he left BRM to devote his full time to farming in Derbyshire. MK

A VICTIM OF CIRCUMSTANCE

Barney Oldfield and his Green Dragon made the name of the Peerless which otherwise had a steady, but unspectacular, history during its thirty years of production

THE FIRST MOTOR CAR produced by the Peerless Manufacturing Company, of Cleveland, Ohio, was a typical 'horseless carriage' and was fitted with bicycle wheels and a single-cylinder De Dion-Bouton engine. Prior to this, the company had been makers of clothes wringers and bicycles, but, like so many turn-of-the-century companies, it was quick to see the potential of the new-fangled automobile. From this inauspicious start, the company developed and eventually became known as 'One of the three Ps', the other two being the Packard and Pierce-Arrow concerns.

Peerless followed up their original prototype with a $3\frac{1}{2}$ hp single-cylinder, water-cooled model known as the Type C Motorette, which, in those days (1901), sold for $1300. This was augmented later in the year by the cheaper and smaller Type B.

The arrival, during 1901, of Louis P. Mooers as Chief Designer was to have an important bearing upon the history of Peerless, which, up to that time, had had little impact upon the motoring scene in America. It was Mooers who was to shape company policy during its early years, and it was he who designed the 1902 Peerless range. These cars were shaft driven and had their engines mounted vertically in the front. Although this layout was later to become almost universally accepted, it was, in those days, a great innovation and immediately drew the public's attention to the Peerless name. The models also used selective sliding-gear transmission and side-entrance tonneaus. It is thought that Peerless were perhaps the first company to market their cars with this type of tonneau. Although the prototypes of the 1902 model range used single-cylinder Mooer-designed engines, the actual production models appeared with twin-cylinder power units.

For 1903, Louis P. Mooers designed an 80 hp four-cylinder engine for use in a lightweight racing car. The engine was designed with a T-head, and lubrication was fully pressurised. The car was entered in the 1903 Gordon Bennett Cup, where it was driven by Mooers. Its competition début, however, was far from encouraging and the car retired on lap two after averaging only 19.8 mph. Undaunted, Mooers returned to production cars and produced two new machines, a 24 hp and a 35 hp, both with T-head four-cylinder engines. That year also saw Peerless introduce their Limousine, a car which is now considered to be America's first non-custom-built closed car.

In 1904, Mooers, determined to improve on his poor showing the previous year, designed another racing car. It was, in fact, the 1903 Gordon Bennett car, rebuilt and fitted with a 6 in bore × 6 in stroke engine. Christened the *Green Dragon* by its owner, Barney Oldfield, to whom the car had passed after failing to qualify for the 1904 Gordon Bennett, it was to establish the Peerless name in no uncertain manner. Oldfield, nicknamed the 'Boy in Green', acted as test driver for the company's racing cars. He was a natural showman and was soon attracting attention at race

tracks all over America. Time and again he set new lap records and, in so doing, established both his name and that of the Peerless *Green Dragon* in the history books of American motor sport. He crashed *Green Dragon* in 1905, but a new car was soon built and, once again, Oldfield continued on his winning way.

The publicity gained by Oldfield and *Green Dragon* did wonders for the Peerless company. By this time, Peerless was rapidly expanding and it soon began to increase production; with the new-found fame came a new image. The Peerless became regarded as a prestige vehicle and was given a price tag to match. In 1907, the model range was boosted with the introduction of a six-cylinder model, although the faithful four-cylinder models continued in production for a few more years, and changes were limited to perfection of details. By 1912, the Peerless model range contained vehicles priced from $4200 to $7200 and the following year saw the introduction of Peerless-designed self starters to all models.

The next big step in the company's history took place in 1915 with the arrival of a Peerless V8. Because the V8 was so reasonably priced, Peerless decided to drop the six-cylinder models from its range. In

Above: a 1904 Peerless four-seater runabout. It was powered by a four-cylinder, 3720 cc engine

Above right: after the Mercer Raceabout style was this six-cylinder 60.6 hp Model 32 of 1911

Right: a Peerless show display of 1926

Peerless

Right: a 1926 Peerless

Below: a Peerless 16 prototype, with coachwork by Pininfarina, seen in 1932

appearance, the V8 resembled the Cadillac which had appeared on the market a year before. The V8 was a strong and well made engine capable of producing 80 bhp at 2700 rpm. It continued in production until 1922, by which time the car's body design had become outdated. In the interim, Peerless had continued to establish themselves as makers of top-quality cars and their products were enjoying steady if unspectacular success. The follow-up design to the original V8 first appeared in 1923 and, like its predecessor, looked not unlike the Cadillac of the day, an indication of the market at which Peerless were aiming their new creation.

Peerless range ever produced. Three six-cylinder models and one eight were offered at prices ranging from $995 to $2195.

Alas, the cars came at the wrong time. By the early 1930s, America was gripped by the Depression and car sales began to plummet. The Peerless company slipped to 30th place in the US sales charts and the company was never really to recover from the damage done to its finances and its reputation during this period. Nevertheless, Peerless were determined to stage a fightback and, in an attempt to recapture its former glory, the company introduced a fabulous new model designed to rival the Cadillac and Marmon sixteen-cylinder

By 1923, Peerless were enjoying the fruits of their labour with some 5000 cars being sold. Twelve months later, the company began producing another six-cylinder model as a companion to the larger and more expensive 'V' model, which by now had been graced with the title of the 'Equipoised Eight'. Another new model was introduced in 1925 and it, too, was a six-cylinder: the engine was a Continental—the first time the company had used a non-Peerless-designed engine—and it was fitted to a 6–80 chassis. By this time, the company was catering for a fairly wide section of the motoring market and prices ranged from $1400 for the least expensive six-cylinder model to more than $4000 for the most expensive eight.

Sales, however, began to fall from 1926 until 1929. The reason for this was that Peerless bodies were beginning to look a little out of date. In fact, many critics considered them to be uninspired and downright unattractive. The company, however, were determined to stop the decline and in 1929 a completely redesigned model range was shown to the public. The old V8 engine had been dropped, and in its place was the more powerful and up-to-date Continental V8 power unit. Considerable attention had also been paid to body design, and the new cars bore a passing resemblance to the then in-vogue Stutz and Marmon products. Within a few months, sales had once again begun to pick up and Peerless decided to capitalise on the situation by commissioning Count Alexis de Sakhnoffsky to design their 1930 range. This he did and the result was the sleekest and best looking

Above: a 1904 Peerless competing in the 1974 London-to-Brighton car rally. The Peerless company was one of the earliest American motor manufacturers and built cars from 1901 until 1931

models. This new car was the Peerless V16. Marmon and Cadillac were two of only three manufacturers to market sixteen-cylinder models (the other being, of course, Bugatti with its type 47) and Peerless were determined to enter this high-prestige market. Unfortunately, conditions were against it and only one prototype Peerless V16 was ever built. This car, in fact, still survives today. It was a pity that the V16 was never marketed because the car possessed tremendous potential. It was built almost entirely of aluminium and the frame weighed a mere 42 lb. The giant 7.6-litre engine produced 173 bhp at 3300 rpm, and its body, coachbuilt by Murphy, was one of the most handsome ever to appear on an American car.

The Depression, however, had destroyed any hope of putting the V16 on the market and it was also the cause of the eventual failure of the Peerless Motor Car Company which closed its doors on 30 June 1931. The factory then lay idle for some time. Thereafter, prohibition having been repealed, the company became the Peerless Corporation, brewers of Carling's Ale, a company still in operation in 1975.

The Peerless name was revived briefly in Britain during the years 1957 to 1960. This came about when a sporty grand-touring car was marketed by a company, established in the mid 1920s, which had originally sold reconditioned Peerless lorries after World War I. Like its American counterpart, this company also failed and so the Peerless name was added to the long list of manufacturers who have become victims of circumstances they could not control.   MW

THE RICART DIAMOND AND THE FLYING HORSE

The Pegaso was a jewel of a motor car. It was perhaps too far advanced
for its time and was therefore doomed to failure right from the beginning

'WE IN SPAIN,' said Señor Carreras of ENASA, 'are poor people making jewels for the rich'. It was late 1951, and the Pegaso car newly introduced by his firm answered his description perfectly. The very high price of the car confirmed that it was exclusively for the rich, and the elaborate specification and superb workmanship qualified it as a jewel of a car, a jewel of outstanding quality and exceptional rarity.

It seemed a curious thing for ENASA to produce. Their full name was Empresa Nacional de Auto-camiones SA, or National Lorry Manufacturing Company. Their principal business was not in making jewels for the rich, but buses for the relatively poor, and lorries, too—all carrying the emblem of Pegasus, the flying horse. The factory in which they worked was of no less surprising origin: it was where those noble Hispano-Suiza cars were made from 1910 (when the original factory near the centre of Barcelona proved too small) until the Spanish Hispano-Suiza company came to its end in 1944. It was a very complete and

spotlessly clean factory in which the assembly of the Pegaso engine was conducted as though it were a surgical operation. The firm's technicians maintained the strictest control over every little component—and indeed almost everything in the vehicles was made on the spot. Such things as steering gears, transmissions, springs and all the many other parts that other manu-facturers buy from outside suppliers, were made by ENASA themselves; they even worked out in their own laboratories how to make aluminium bearings, a secret formerly known only to a few German tech-nologists, but important to Spain because of the then shortage of copper—an ironic situation in a country that had been the ancient world's main source of it, where the Rio Tinto used to run red with the stain of the metal.

In such conditions, it would be relatively easy to produce in small numbers a superb car, and the de-cision to undertake it was based on an unusual motive: it was not primarily to make money, but to train

Above: in 1953, Pegaso produced these two models both styled by Touring of Milan. On the right is the model known as 'Thrill' while alongside it stands the Z103 which was available with pushrod V8 engines of 4, 4.5 or 4.7 litres. Only a handful of these Z103s were built

apprentices. There, as in other factories, newcomers to the industry's crafts had to learn to work to the very highest standards: they would necessarily work slowly, and the reject rate would be high, but the workpieces that emerged would be far superior to anything that might be seen coming from an ordinary mass-production factory. Why not give them something interesting to work on, something suitably small in scale, something that would attract attention and approval from all sides, such as might improve the reputation of the company and thus aid its sales of heavy vehicles?

To design the car they had Wilfredo Ricart, who had been with Alfa Romeo from 1936 until 1945. He was a

road-going body and equipment. Indeed, when the first car to be shown to the public appeared at the Paris Salon in the autumn of 1951, its engine capacity of 2474 cc was remarked on as fitting the limit for Grand Prix racing from 1954 onwards; and when the course for the Spanish Grand Prix a few weeks later was opened by three Pegasos driven round it at a spanking pace, people could not forebear to ask whether Pegaso might enter the lists of racing. At Grand Prix level, they never did, while in sports-car events they were modest in most of their ambitions and attainments. In their intended rôle as very fast road cars, though, they quickly acquired a reputation that entirely justi-

Spaniard, born in 1898, with a history of design including sports cars, racing cars and diesel engines; and during his period with Alfa Romeo he added a 28-cylinder aero engine to his record, and a V16 three-litre Grand Prix car whose engine incorporated 64 valves, five superchargers, two carburettors, and roller bearings everywhere. He was one of those extraordinary engineers who make a fetish of doing things thoroughly or not at all, and he antagonised Ferrari so much when he went to Alfa Romeo that Ferrari soon left. Ricart used to wear shoes with exceedingly thick rubber soles, and when Ferrari one day asked him why, Ricart replied that a great engineer's brain must be carefully sprung against the inequalities of the ground, in case its delicate mechanism were disturbed.

The mechanism was still functioning well a decade later, when he returned to his homeland and to the design of the Pegaso. The car had the most mouthwatering specification of any in the world, being tantamount to a de-tuned Grand Prix racer with

fied the promise of their specifications.

The first model was the Z102, and was a sensation. Its V8 engine (bore 75 mm, stroke 70 mm) had dry-sump lubrication, four overhead camshafts and one, two or four Weber carburettors. Fuel being still of poor quality in those days, the standard compression ratio was 7.5:1, but the engine nevertheless gave a minimum of 170 bhp at 6300 rpm, with considerably more to come from higher compression and elaborate carburation. The gearbox was a five-speed close-ratio dog-engaged type integral with the final drive, which incorporated a limited-slip differential of the ZF type. Around this transmission complex was arranged the rear suspension, of reversed de Dion type: the dead axle beam passed in front of the transmission, and was located by a pair of radius arms which converged on a single point well to the rear. Thus, the motion of the axle was geometrically purer than that of any other de Dion axle of the time (or for many years later), while the suspension loads could be taken out at widely separated points: thrust and braking forces were fed through the rear pivot, spring loads transmitted through linkages to torsion bars, anchored to the chassis ahead of the rear axle. Torsion bars also featured at the front, where the wheels were independently mounted on paired wishbones. All four wheels carried copiously ventilated brakes of exceptional size and power, the fourteen-inch drums housing Lockheed components that—together with the Bosch ignition and the Borrani aluminium-rimmed wheels—were practically the only components of foreign origin. The Pirelli tyres were made in Spain and were of generous size by the standards of the day, combining with the excellence of the suspension and the carefully arranged distribution of masses to give the Pegaso superb handling. The Pegaso was one of those well balanced cars that could

Above: the V8 Pegaso engine was introduced in 1951 and was of very sophisticated design for that time. It had four overhead camshafts, dry-sump lubrication and one, two or four Weber carburettors. Over a period of years it was used with various cylinder capacities ranging from 2472 cc to 3178 cc

be driven in whatever style the driver chose to dictate, its relatively short wheelbase of 92 inches and its high polar moments of inertia in pitch and yaw giving it a balance akin to that of current Grand Prix cars, while its suspension geometry was actually superior. Only in its chassis was its design questionable: this was a multi-tubular fabrication vased on square-section steel tubes and was amply rigid at each end, but beam and torsional stiffness appeared to be compromised in the shallowest part of the chassis under the door sills at mid wheelbase.

The choice of carburettors and compression ratios was the prelude to a proliferation of changes and options that followed in rapid succession. The Z102B had its cylinder bores enlarged to give 2.8 litres displacement and 210 bhp; the Z102SS went even further with 3.2 litres and anything from 210 to 280 bhp for, by this time, any of the cars could be supplied with a Roots supercharger. One of the blown cars, with a quite simple open two-seater body, covered the flying mile in Belgium at 152.001 mph in 1953, by which time the make had already made some tentative forays into motor sport. It was a Pegaso that set a new record for the hill-climb at Rabassada. By 1953, the company felt tempted to enter a pair of cars for Le Mans, and built very special asymmetrical versions of the blown 2.8 for the purpose. They were faintly reminiscent of Taruffi's twin-boom record-breaking cars, but one crashed in practice for the race, killing the driver, Jover, and the other was withdrawn. In the following year, a Pegaso owned by the son of Cuba's President Trujillo was driven by Joaquin Palacio in the formidable Carrera PanAmericana; it had mounted to second place overall when it was eliminated by somebody else's accident.

If mechanical specifications could be so variable, the variety of bodies carried by the Pegaso was even more noteworthy. The firm's own standard body, a two-seater GT coupé in the Italian idiom, was nevertheless distinctive in appearance and quite handsome, very simple and almost severe in its external appearance. This sobriety was reflected by the firm's advertising, which always appeared as a masterpiece of elegance and understatement; but if an owner chose, the interior of the car could be just as severe, for the all-up weight of the fully trimmed and sturdy standard car could be reduced from 24 cwt to near the bare ton, by drastic pruning which left nothing more than a flock spray to decorate the inner surfaces of the body panels. Much the most outstanding bodies, however, were created by the great custom builders of the day, notable contributions being made by Saoutchik of Paris and by Touring of Milan. The latter showed in 1953 a Berlinetta that they christened *Thrill*, and it was surely one of the most *chic* productions ever: form-fitting seats and lap straps were a feature of the interior, but the most notable device took the form of a pair of airfoil-section 'flying buttresses', extending from the hips to the shoulders of the roof, just behind the side windows. These were claimed to control the boundary-layer air flow around the sides of the canopy and over the extensively glazed tapering tail, and they were blended into the body panels with impeccable smoothness, the finish on this body being quite exceptional.

In another sense, the finish of the Pegaso was unfortunately nearer than could be anticipated. After producing yet more variants, known as the Z103, with pushrod V8 engines of 4, 4.5 and 4.7 litres, Ricart retired in 1958 and the policy of the company then changed in favour of concentrating on the heavy vehicles that had always been its mainstay. Only three or four Z103 cars were made, and only 125 Z102s, mostly to special order. Perhaps this was as it should have been: jewels lose their allure when they become superabundant.   LJKS

Above: a 1954 Pegaso V8 sports-racing car. That year saw a Pegaso prove competitive in the gruelling Carrera Pan-Americana race. Owned by the son of Cuba's President Trujillo, and driven by Joaquin Palacio, the car mounted to second place overall before being eliminated by somebody else's accident

A MECHANICAL CHARLATAN

Edward Joel Pennington was a smooth-tongued inventor whose imagination often seemed to get the better of his judgement

IT WOULD BE DIFFICULT to find a better synonym for Edward Joel Pennington than that coined by the pioneer motorist and patent agent Eric W. Walford, who called this glib-tongued American inventor a 'mechanical charlatan'. As Walford handled many of Pennington's improbable patents, he was well qualified to judge! The name of Pennington dominated the motoring press in the years 1895–96, and his claims were regarded with great seriousness.

E. J. Pennington first came to the public notice in 1890, when he was 32, by promoting a fanciful airship: his dreams of mechanical flight earned him the nickname 'Airship' Pennington. 'Supposing,' he would say, 'I have a cycle, screw-driven, making a mile a minute; just suppose that; then suppose I put aeroplanes on that machine, and they are well arranged and under good control, what then?'

By 1893, however, he had become obsessed with the internal-combustion engine, and the following year persuaded Thomas Kane & Company of Chicago, who had been building light marine engines since 1885 to finance his experiments, and soon the first Kane-Pennington power unit was complete. Even by the unformed standards of the period, the Kane-Pennington was unorthodox, for its drawn-steel-tube cylinders had only a minimum of water jacketing—indeed, in its smaller forms, the Kane-Pennington had no water-jacket or cooling fins at all; and no carburettor, just a primitive drip-feed device. Pennington's explanation of how the engine worked had a distinctly improbable air: 'All fluids take up a vast amount of heat in the change of vapour, and as my engine has no carburettor,

but vapourises the charge directly in the cylinder, the fluid in vapourising absorbs the heat the cylinder walls have derived from the last explosion, and thus keeps the heat of the cylinders at a comparatively low point.

'The charge is exploded only when the effective stroke crank angle is 45 degrees, and previous to the delivery of the igniting spark to the charge, a mingling current of electricity is put through the air and gas in the cylinder, and by virtue of this non-igniting current delivered to the mixture, the heat absorption power or capacity, one or both, of gas in the cylinder is so incredibly augmented that the cylinder temperature can be, and actually is, so greatly lowered that the walls of the cylinders are kept cool to within convenient working limits.'

Such specious claptrap greatly impressed the *soi-disant* technical journalists of the day, who were eminently capable of being gulled by anyone who could

Below: the amazing Pennington Torpedo Autocar of 1896. This machine was supposed to have been able to carry nine people, although where they were meant to have been seated remains a mystery. It had a top speed of about 40 mph

use longer words than they, and the Kane-Pennington engine was afforded wide coverage in the technical press, including an article in *The American Machinist* for 7 November 1895, which gave Henry Ford technical inspiration for the power unit of his Quadricycle.

Pennington claimed to have built a petrol car as early as 1894, a curious-looking 'Victoria' apparently concocted from two cycle frames joined by tubular cross-members. Utterly devoid of springing, the car was mounted on a typical Pennington feature, giant pneumatic tyres claimed to be unpuncturable. The all-up weight of this curious machine was 400 lb, and its twin-cylinder engine was reported to be capable of propelling the car at 20–25 mph. Not only that, but the ingenious Pennington claimed that, thanks to the 'long-mingling spark', the engine would run on

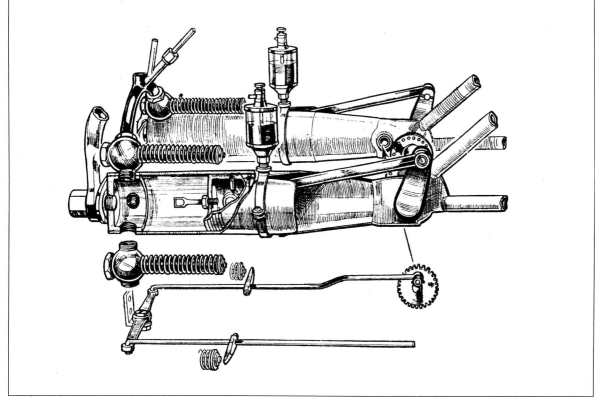

Above: in 1898, the world saw the introduction of this 'Fighting Autocar', ready for attacking from the front and parrying advances from the rear. The vehicle had a stroke of 12 in and was often seen trundling menacingly around Richmond Park

Left: the parallel-twin engine of the Pennington Torpedo; shown at the bottom is its valve gear. The only control on this engine for the driver was an ignition switch. Note the long stroke, which was 305 mm

ordinary paraffin, and purported to prove the fact by testing the fuel with a densimeter. In fact, he used the very best, most volatile, petroleum, and a densimeter with faked graduations!

Another of Pennington's early products was a motor cycle which was said to be capable of such phenomenal speeds—'from 6 to 50 mph'—that it had hit a bump and sailed through the air for 65 feet, whereupon Pennington issued an advertisement showing the cycle leaping a river, to the consternation of various passers-by and boatmen!

The Victoria had minimal water jackets on its engine, but the cycle's power unit was devoid of any form of cooling. The only control over the engine speed on either vehicle was a metering device which controlled the amount of petrol dribbled into the cylinder, plus an ignition switch. The engine of the cycle used the rear wheel spindle as its crankshaft, and thus drove direct, but the Victoria had a simple two-speed gear.

Despite the performance claims made for the Pennington vehicles, their inventor did not enter for the *Chicago Times-Herald* race from Milwaukee to

Chicago for a purse of $5000 on 2 November 1895. He claimed that it was the policy of the Kane-Pennington concern to supply motors only—not complete vehicles—to the public. He stated: 'It is quite probable that several entries in the Milwaukee-Chicago race will be driven by Kane-Pennington motors, as the leading cycle makers have ordered motors of this type'. Not one Pennington-engined vehicle appeared on the starting line, though. One factor in this policy of non-appearance may have been the very strict scientific tests carried out on the competing vehicles by the organisers, which would have revealed the fake densimeter dodge.

Two weeks after the *Times-Herald* race, Pennington sailed for England, where Harry J. Lawson had just paid 'a very large sum, a larger sum, we believe, than has ever been paid for any other petroleum motor patent', to secure English rights for his British Motor Syndicate; the actual figure was around £100,000.

Pennington was allotted one floor of Lawson's newly acquired Motor Mills at Coventry as part of Lawson's million-pound Great Horseless Carriage Company, which publicised extravagant plans for large-scale production of all types of motor vehicles (although it seems as though most of the capital found its way into the pockets of Lawson and his somewhat shady cronies).

The true facts behind the Great Horseless Carriage Company were not up to the advertised claims: A

party had been brought down from London by special train to verify the mere existence of this alleged new industry. On the ground floor of the factory they saw men busily at work. After due inspection, they proceeded up curtained stairs to the first floor, where a halt was called in a partitioned space and light refreshments were proferred. Then the work doing on the first floor was inspected. The same process was repeated on proceeding to the second floor; some visitors, more curious than the rest, who ascended the

Top: Pennington's transport for good friends, *circa* 1896. The friends are seen at Nunhead Grounds

Above: Crystal Palace is the scene of introduction for this car of 1898

curtained stairway, being now conscious of an echo of footsteps at the opposite end of the building. After yet another pause for refreshments, on emerging from the partitioned space, the visitors were conducted round the second floor, whereupon one of the Paul Prys was prompted to enquire whether it was the policy of this pioneer company of a new industry to make a point of recruiting members of the same families, placing brothers to work on different floors? The answer is not recorded. But there was yet one more storey to which to ascend. The sequence of events was repeated, including the echoing of footfalls from opposite, and the subsequent recognition, this time in a still greater number of cases, of increasingly familiar faces among the operatives.

In fact, Pennington built very few vehicles of any sort, although a prolific flood of projected fire-engines, armoured 'war motors' and other wild schemes was dutifully illustrated in *The Autocar* (whose Editor, Henry Sturmey, just happened to be chairman of the Daimler Motor Company, another tenant of the Motor Mills). Two motor cycles, a single-seater and a tandem, were built by Humber, who also made the frame for the 1896 Pennington Torpedo Autocar. Recalled T. W. Blumfield, who helped build and test the cycles: 'The machine would run from about 8 or 10 miles an hour, its slowest speed, to about 30 miles an hour. There being no compression release or exhaust-valve lifter, and the bore and stroke being $2\frac{1}{2}$ in by 6 in, the difficulties of slow running and starting can be imagined. Although the cylinders were not normally cooled in any way, overheating was not one of the troubles experienced, and it ran as far as, perhaps, 10 miles without a breakdown, although on most occasions the ignition failed very quickly and a new spring wiper had to be fitted.'

The Torpedo was an incredible device. Advertised as being capable of carrying nine people, it was a three-wheeler cycle with an uncooled twin-cylinder engine with a ludicrously long stroke (305 mm) giving a cubic capacity of 1871 cc; it was controlled from the rear saddle (but the forward passenger could also steer if he had a mind to) and had four transverse saddles dotted about its frame. It could achieve 40 mph, beat a Bollée tricar in a (probably rigged) tug-of-war, and retired from the 1896 Emancipation Day London-Brighton Run when one of the 'unpuncturable' tyres burst on the outskirts of London. For some months, Pennington dominated the correspondence columns of *The Autocar*, throwing out wild challenges which were never taken up, and carrying on a running verbal battle with Roots & Venables Limited, who *had* built a car that ran on paraffin, and were not prepared to swallow Pennington's claims.

In the spring of 1897, Pennington floated an Irish Pennington company, which was to open a vast new factory at Ringsend, near Dublin, but the company folded before the works (or a single car) was built, and most of the investors lost their money.

It was obvious that the rich supply of hot air which had kept the Pennington concern buoyant was cooling down. In December 1897, someone signing himself 'Constant Reader'. complained querulously to *The Autocar*: 'The Pennington was to the fore in May and in November is no more to be seen . . . we had the queer-looking four-seated tandem flaunted before us *ad nauseam* and we at least had the right to hope that this wearisome repetition might lead to something good. Apparently the whole thing has gone out like a candle.

'But what about the Pennington patents paid for by the British Motor Syndicate and Great Horseless

Carriage Company. Are they worthless?'

Apparently, dear Constant Reader, they were. At the 1898 National Show at the Crystal Palace, though the irrepressible Pennington was back, with an even more ludicrous car—the Raft Victoria, which had front-wheel drive, rear-wheel steering and final drive by rope (replacement drive ropes could be purchased for half-a-crown, 'ready joined in a continuous piece with a long splice').

The projected price of this oddity was £100, but more than 400 feckless autocarists placed orders for the vehicle, so Pennington (satirised by American author George Randolph Chester as 'Get-Rich-Quick Wallingford') promptly upped the figure to £115 10s! He still failed to deliver a single vehicle to a private buyer. A de luxe version, with sprung bodywork, was introduced in 1899 by John Stirling of Stirling's Motor Carriages of Lanarkshire, who commented: 'The "Universal" car is designed and built for a double purpose—for use as a pleasure vehicle, and also as a light parcel car. It is arranged with movable or folding hind seat, and portable back wing for use as parcel car . . . the whole of the space under the seats, with a cubic capacity of between seven and eight cubic feet, is available for the carriage of luggage, etc. This storage room is extremely useful, and is, indeed, a more necessary essential in a motor car than in a horse-drawn vehicle.' As the body of the Stirling-Pennington was sprung on three 'graduated steel springs' and the control levers were fixed to the un-sprung chassis (the steering tiller moved fore-and-aft), handling the beast must have been near impossible, so it is as well that only one of these vehicles was built. Hubert W. Egerton, who was well known for his

marathon drives of unlikely vehicles, attempted to motor from Manchester to London with a Pennington Raft, but abandoned the car at Nuneaton in a fit of frustration after fitting no less than 72 replacement sparking plugs!

At the end of 1899, Pennington returned to America where, in conjunction with Lawson, he launched the Anglo-American Rapid Vehicle Company, with a capital of $75 million and the rights to 200 motor vehicle patents of dubious value. A few four-wheeled Torpedos were built, and the company claimed an order for 1000 of these vehicles to be used by the British Army in the Boer War. However, the Lawson-Pennington empire collapsed faster than the investors' pockets could be emptied, and Pennington dropped out of sight for a while—and Lawson spent some time in jail for his financial chicanery.

Over the next decade, Pennington's name cropped up from time to time in connection with increasingly more far-fetched schemes, and when he died, in 1911, he was in the process of sueing the manufacturers of the Indian Motor cycle for infringing his invention of the self-propelled two-wheeler!

Pennington activities had been largely responsible for causing a slump in the motor-manufacturing industry at the end of the 19th Century, yet this man who helped to part the public from some millions of pounds, probably built less than twenty vehicles of all kinds in his egregious career, yet beneath all the bluff, Pennington undoubtedly possessed a genuine talent which properly channelled, might have made a lasting contribution to the development of the motor vehicle. Now he will only be remembered as a smooth-tongued confidence trickster.   DBW

Above: Edward Joel Pennington sits proudly on his Torpedo in 1896. Pennington, 'imposter par excellence', claimed he owned the largest motor vehicle company in the world, but it was nothing more than a small firm with outlandish ideas that were hardly ever likely to transform the industry in the way he would have liked

The name of the game is winning

THE PENSKE STORY begins with Roger Penske the youthful racing driver, and develops into Roger Penske the millionaire businessman and Grand Prix car builder. It spans many years and contains an element of intrigue, for Penske has not always divulged everything, especially where United States factory support is concerned.

Of German descent (his grandfather came from Leipzig), Roger Penske was born in Philadelphia on 20 February 1937. His wealthy father was vice-president of a warehousing firm and taught Roger early to earn his money. At the age of nine, he and his father became regular attenders at the Akron Sportsman's Park, watching midget-car racing. He said, 'We went for years. It was built into my blood, and I knew I'd race some day.'

At the age of fourteen, he borrowed sufficient money to buy a Norton motor cycle, a machine used for Penske's newspaper round. After a serious accident, though, when a parked car pulled out in front of him and he spent twelve weeks in hospital, he bought an MG TD and began working for a foreign-car dealer when not at university. Soon, Penske became involved in buying and selling cars, and worked for Ben Moore, a Chevrolet dealer. Moore encouraged Penske to take up racing himself and at the age of twenty he took to the tracks with a Jaguar XK 120, also competing in hill-climbs. As soon as he was 21, he became eligible to compete in Sports Car Club of America events and he went to a racing drivers' school at Marlboro. His tutors

were two well-known competitors, Dick Thompson and Fred Windridge, and in a weekend they shaped him into a capable driver. At that time Penske used a Chevrolet Corvette and by the end of the weekend, which included two trial races, it was becoming tired. However, it survived three further races in 1958—including a victory at Berwick—before it was sold in September when Roger married Lissa Stouffer, a restaurant heiress.

At the end of 1958, Penske traded in a gullwing Mercedes-Benz 300SL to purchase his first pure racing machine, the ex-Bob Holbert Porsche RS. It provided Penske with some success, but when attending the Sebring 12-hours early in 1959 he saw the latest works Porsches and decided the RS was too uncompetitive. He bought a Porsche RSK and, co-driving with Harry Blanchard, won the Sundown 6-hours at Harewood, Ontario.

The exciting world of Roger Penske: being interviewed at Brands Hatch, *left*; picking the brains of Graham Hill and Mario Andretti, *below*; the F1 Penske PC1 in action, Mark Donohue at the wheel, *bottom*

Later, Penske teamed with Skip Callanan and won the 8-hour 'Little Le Mans' at Lime Rock in a Fiat-Abarth. In 1960, he battled with Bob Holbert for the Class F SCCA National Championship, among his successes being victory in all three heats of the Carling 300 at Harewood, ahead of Olivier Gendebien, Pete Ryan and Holbert. At the very end of the year, he purchased a Porsche RS60 from Jim Hall for the rich professional races at Riverside and Laguna Seca, but for once his luck turned sour.

In 1961, teamed with Holbert, Penske finished fifth overall in the Sebring 12-hours and won the Index of Performance handicap section. He chatted with Cooper works driver Bruce McLaren and decided to order a Cooper T57 Monaco–Climax sports car and a Formula One Cooper T55–Climax. Both were delivered in August and until then he raced a Maserati T61, the 'Birdcage' model, winning at Elkhart Lake, Lime Rock and Meadowvale. In October, he took part in the United States Grand Prix at Watkins Glen against chiefly European opposition, finishing a good eighth in his Formula One Cooper. Penske concluded the year with fine performances at Laguna Seca, Riverside and in the Nassau Speed Week with the Cooper Monaco. He won the Class D SCCA National Championship plus the Most Improved Driver of the Year award.

Then came a new episode in the life of Penske. The BS degree in industrial management, gained at Lehigh University in 1959, had not been won for nothing. While at Nassau, Penske had noticed an advertisement on the side of a fellow competitor's Ferrari and promptly wrote a five-page letter to DuPont, who handled Telar and Zerex antifreeze, suggesting he could run under their name. The deal came off and Penske's cars became known as Telar or Zerex Specials.

Early in 1962, Penske visited Briggs Cunningham, for whom he was to drive a Maserati-engined Cooper Monaco in the Sebring 12-hours, and in a corner he spotted the wreckage of the Formula One Cooper T55–Climax crashed by Walt Hansgen in the previous October's United States Grand Prix. In exchange for some Maserati parts, Penske became the owner of the wreckage and, with the aid of Roy Gane, Penske's chief mechanic, he straightened the frame and rebuilt the car as a single-seater sports-racer. A very light machine, scaling at 1100 lb, it was powered by a 2.7-litre Coventry Climax FPF engine and clothed in an aluminium body, a contribution from Penske's post-college employer, Alcoa. Known as the Zerex Special, it won three major races at Riverside, Laguna Seca and Puerto Rico, beating top American and European entries, but it caused controversy as its centrally placed seat contravened FIA Appendix C sports-car regulations. However, the United States Auto Club, which sanctioned the races, had previously declared it legal. Earlier in the year, Penske had campaigned his Cooper T57 Monaco–Climax successfully to win the East Coast SCCA Championship; he also ventured to Europe, to Brands Hatch on August Bank Holiday Monday, finishing fifth in the Guards Trophy to Mike Parkes, Innes Ireland, Jo Bonnier and Carlo Mario Abate. With his Formula One Cooper T55–Climax, now with a 2.7-litre engine, he was second in the Pipeline

200 to Dan Gurney and won the first heat of the Hoosier Grand Prix.

For 1963, Penske modified the Zerex Special to two-seater specification and brought it to Brands Hatch for the Guards Trophy once more. This time he walked away with the race, conquering the best European sports cars. He also drove a 4-litre Ferrari 330 TR/LM with Pedro Rodriguez in the Le Mans 24-hours, but retired, and in the Tourist Trophy at Goodwood he was a disappointed eighth in a special-bodied Ferrari 250 GTO. Earlier in the year, he had co-driven a Ferrari 250 GTO with Augie Pabst in the Sebring 12-hours, finishing fourth overall and winning the GT section. At the end of 1963, Penske found the Zerex Special becoming uncompetitive, beaten by lightweight machines powered by V8 American engines. He switched to John Mecom's team, driving a Chevrolet-engined Cooper and a Chevrolet Corvette Grand Sport V8 coupé.

Early in 1964, Penske gave up his job at Alcoa to take over a General Motors agency in Philadelphia. He joined the General Motors-backed Chaparral team, taking second place at Riverside, winning at Laguna Seca and in two of the three major events in the Nassau Speed Week—he won the third, too, in a Chevrolet Corvette Grand Sport. At the end of the year, having already signed up to drive for Chaparral again in 1965, Penske suddenly announced his retirement from race driving. He gave the pressures of his expanded business operations and family responsibilities as his reasons, but added, 'I hope to be able to sponsor a car one day, just to keep my hand in'.

Just over a year later, in 1966, Penske was back. He entered a Chevrolet Corvette in the Daytona 24 hours which won the GT award, and he persuaded the Sun Oil Company to sponsor a Lola T70-Chevrolet sports car to be driven by Penske's protégé, a shy motor engineer aged 29, Mark Donohue. Donohue proved a wise choice, winning the Mosport round in the new Can-Am Challenge Cup series and taking an eventual second place on points to John Surtees. Soon, Donohue began to work full time for Penske, preparing the cars as well as driving them. Racing Penske's Lola T70–Chevrolet, Donohue won the 1967 US Road Racing Championship sports-car series. The programme escalated the following year: with an ex-works McLaren M6A–Chevrolet, Donohue won the US Road Racing Championship for the second year running and was third in the Can-Am Challenge Cup behind the works McLarens of Denny Hulme and Bruce McLaren. In the Trans-Am Championship, a manufacturers' series for 5-litre saloon cars, Penske renewed his acquaintance with General Motors' Engineering & Development Division by campaigning Chevrolet Camaros. Sure enough, with Donohue doing the lion's share of the driving, Chevrolet triumphed in Trans-Am in both 1968 and 1969, taking twenty victories from 27 starts.

In 1969, Penske withdrew from the Can-Am series to concentrate on winning the Trans-Am, plus a new venture: an entry in the Indianapolis 500. Donohue, at the wheel of the four-wheel-drive Lola T152 Offenhauser, qualified fourth fastest and finished seventh, also gaining the Rookie of the Year award. In February, Penske entered a Lola T70 Mk 3B–Chevrolet coupé in

the Daytona 24-hours, Mark Donohue/Chuck Parsons steering it to victory despite several problems. This was to have been a prelude for a Penske-masterminded, General Motors-backed attack on the Le Mans 24-hours in June. Indeed, four works Lolas were entered for the race, but in April the project was cancelled. Another link with General Motors was the testing of a stock-block Chevrolet-engined Lola at Indianapolis, but it proved uncompetitive.

In October 1969, Penske dropped a bombshell on the racing world. He announced he would be running American Motors Javelins in the 1970 Trans-Am series. Penske had arranged a lucrative deal with American Motors and used his team's engineering expertise to transform the Javelins into race winners. In the 1970 series, they were second to Ford, but in 1971 the title was theirs.

During 1970, Penske once more attempted Indianapolis, this time Donohue managing second in a Lola T153–Ford. A brief, end-of-season flirtation in Formula 5000 saw Donohue winning three races in the prototype Lola T190–Chevrolet. 1971, though, was a more ambitious year. Penske was prosperous and it showed in his business and motor-racing activities. By now, he had Chevrolet dealerships in Allentown and Detroit as well as Philadelphia. He was involved in a major Hertz rental franchise, in insurance, a chain of Sunoco petrol stations and Goodyear tyre dealerships. He was an automotive consultant to Sears, Roebuck & Co, developing and endorsing a line of high-performance parts, accessories and equipment sold as Penske High Performance Products. He was elected a director of the United States Auto Club, was a director of the Ontario Motor Speedway and vice-chairman of the board of Atlantic City Raceway.

On the racing front, however, apart from the Trans-Am series win, plans fell flat in 1971. With Kirk F. White, a Philadelphia foreign-car dealer, Penske entered a superbly prepared Ferrari 512M in the Daytona 24-hours, Sebring 12-hours, Le Mans 24-hours and Watkins Glen 6-hours, but each time niggling problems let down drivers Mark Donohue and David Hobbs. At Indianapolis, Donohue appeared in a McLaren M16–Offenhauser (Penske switched from Lola to McLaren, undertaking the Colnbrook company's pre-race development programme) and led the race until his gearbox failed. Later, another car smashed into the stranded McLaren, while Penske's second entry of the old Lola driven by David Hobbs was also written-off in an accident. As consolation, Donohue won the Pocono 500 in the rebuilt McLaren later in the year. Penske also tested the Formula One scene, hiring a works McLaren M19A–Ford for Donohue to drive in the Canadian and United States Grands Prix. The car was thoroughly tested prior to the races in the typical Penske tradition and Donohue was a superb third in Canada; he was unable to start in America owing to a postponed USAC event and Hobbs drove the car into 10th place.

In 1972, following visits to Italy, Japan and Germany to talk to Ferrari, Toyota and Porsche, Penske returned to Can-Am to compete with works-assisted, turbocharged Porsche 917–10Ks. Sponsorship came from L & M cigarettes, and the cars, raced by Donohue and George Follmer, proved almost unbeatable. Follmer won the

Above: Roger Penske entered the world of Formula One, as a constructor, with this car designed by Briton Geoff Ferris. Driven by Mark Donohue, the car was known as the First National City Travelers Checks Penske PC1-Ford

Above: the Penske-entered Lola T70, winner at Daytona in 1969

Right: Penske and Donohue in discussion

series, while Donohue, after missing four rounds owing to a mid-season accident, was fourth. Donohue also won the Indianapolis 500 in a Penske-entered McLaren M16B–Offenhauser. An American Motors Matador was prepared for NASCAR racing, but with a 6-litre engine opposing the opposition's 7-litre equipment it was outclassed. Nevertheless, with an imminent change in the regulations it was good groundwork in this very different style of American motor racing.

Donohue annihilated the opposition in the 1973 Can-Am Challenge Cup series, this time driving Penske's Porsche 917–30K, one of the most powerful racing cars ever built, featuring a turbocharged 5.3-litre engine which could be made to develop over 1000 bhp. In effect, this total domination killed Can-Am. Donohue was not so lucky on the USAC trail, however, his Eagle M5–Offenhauser suffering engine failure on every outing, while on the NASCAR front Donohue won the Western 500 in an AM Matador at Riverside. In Formula 5000, a special Lola T330 with an American Motors engine proved uncompetitive when matched against Chevrolet-powered machines, although Donohue managed two seconds in the series and AM reaped technical benefit.

During the winter of 1973–74, Penske promoted a series of races, the International Race of Champions series, for top drivers in all spheres of motor sport. The winner was . . . Mark Donohue following a hectic series of events in Porsche 911 Carreras.

At the end of 1973, news leaked that Penske was to build his own racing car, a Formula One machine. He bought the small, ex-McRae factory in Dorset, England, so as to design and build the car in the hub of Grand Prix racing, Europe. Ex-Brabham designer Geoff Ferris combined his own ideas with those of Penske, Donohue and Don Cox, Penske Racing Inc's director of engineering, and the result, which appeared for the first time in the 1974 Canadian Grand Prix, was a conventional machine using the ubiquitous Ford DFV engine and Hewland gearbox. It was sponsored by First National City Travelers Checks and driven by Mark Donohue, who had emerged from eight months of 'retirement', for after the International Race of Champions series he had supposedly quit and been promoted to president of Penske Racing Inc. Donohue also agreed to drive in 1975.

The 1974 programme also included selected NASCAR events (Bobby Allison won in the Penske Matador at the end-of-season Times 500 at Ontario Motor Speedway) and USAC racing. Over the winter of 1974–75, there was another International Race of Champions series, this time with Chevrolet Camaros, the winner being Bobby Unser. In 1975, the Penske Matador became a strong threat in NASCAR racing, Bobby Allison winning at Riverside and taking second place in the Daytona 500.

Roger Penske's serious and analytical approach to motor racing made his team one of the most successful in the world. He raced to win; indeed, he expected to win. For an American team to enter the basically European Formula arena was a major step. Penske had begun cautiously, knowing he lacked experience of this type of racing, but his aim was to win in the end. MK

FRENCHMAN HENRI PESCAROLO is an acknowledged long-distance sports-car-racing exponent, while he has also shown sufficient 'dash' to be a leading light in Formula Two, yet in Formula One he has never quite made the grade. As with some other top-class drivers, he was never with the right team at the right time.

Henri Pescarolo, the son of a top French surgeon, was born in Montfermeil on 25 September 1942. The serious-looking, bearded medical student was, however, not destined to follow his father's footsteps. Motor sport appealed to him and, after navigating for his father in a doctors' rally in 1964, the following year found him at a racing drivers' school and competing in a Ford-backed series of races for novices in Lotus 7 sports cars. Pescarolo dominated the scene and as a result was invited to partner Jean-Pierre Beltoise and Jean-Pierre Jaussaud in the Formula Three Matra team in 1966.

It was not a successful season for Pescarolo: his car was not ready until the tail-end of the season and then it was beset with small, niggling problems. In 1967, however, Pescarolo proved himself. He won the season's most important Formula Three race at Monaco, gained more wins at Barcelona, La Châtre, Bugatti au Mans, Rouen, Magny-Cours, Nogaro, Zandvoort and Albi and became French Formula Three Champion. Many experts considered he was the best Formula Three driver in Europe. Towards the end of the year, he was twice invited to race a Formula Two Matra and also won a sports-car race at Montlhéry with the 4.7-litre Ford-engined Matra 620.

In 1968, Pescarolo, then 25, was promoted to the Formula Two team full-time, backing up his team-mate Jean-Pierre Beltoise so well that the pair were first and second in the European Formula Two Trophy. Pescarolo won the Albi Grand Prix and finished second five times. In the Le Mans 24-hours, he shared a Matra 630 coupé with Johnny Servoz-Gavin and became the idol of the crowd as he brought the car up to second place. Then, within reach of the lead, the car was put out in the closing stages owing to two punctures and an accident. In September, Pescarolo made his Grand Prix début in the Matra team in the Canadian Grand Prix. Driving one of the raucous V12 Matra MS11s, he retired after half-distance owing to fading oil pressure. He was unable to take part in the United States Grand Prix owing to the lack of an engine, while in Mexico he ran slowly to finish ninth, racing without the Matra's rear wing, owing to a practice accident.

In 1969, Matra gave up Formula One racing, but Pescarolo remained in their Formula Two and sports-car teams. The year began badly with a serious accident during the April Le Mans test weekend when his experimental Matra 640 coupé literally took off at approximately 125 mph down the Mulsanne Straight and crashed heavily. He was thrown from the car and suffered leg and back injuries plus burns. By August, he was back in the cockpit, and on form, winning the Formula Two section of the German Grand Prix in a Matra MS7-Ford. At the end of the year, he shared a Matra 650 with fellow Frenchman Jean-Pierre Beltoise to win the Paris 1000 km sports-car race.

Matra returned to Formula One in 1970,

Sports-car superstar

Below: a very competitive combination; France's Henri Pescarolo and the V12 Matra sports-racing car in action at Watkins Glen

Pescarolo joining Beltoise to drive the new Matra Simca MS120s. The V12 engines seemed to lack the power of their rivals, but Pescarolo was an excellent third in the Monaco Grand Prix, fifth in France and sixth in Belgium and Germany. Apart from an early-season victory in the non championship Buenos Aires 1000 km, the sports-car scene was not so bright, as the Matra Simca 650s were unreliable and underpowered compared with the 5-litre Porsches and Ferraris. At the end of the year, however, Pescarolo drove for Alfa Romeo in the Österreichring 1000 km and finished second, partnered by Andrea de Adamich. In Formula Two, he raced a Brabham BT30-Ford owned by Bob Gerard, finishing second at Barcelona and Pau.

After Matra dropped Pescarolo for 1971, the Frenchman signed to race for Frank Williams in both Formula One and Formula Two, finding support from the French Motul oil company, and for Alfa Romeo in sports-car racing. Apart from a second in the non-championship Argentine Grand Prix and a fourth in the British Grand Prix, Pescarolo's season with Williams' Formula One Marches was dismal. In Formula Two, the year began with victory at Mallory Park in March, only to be followed by a string of retirements. In sports-car racing, Pescarolo found the Alfa Romeo T33/3 fast and reliable, winning the BOAC 1000 km at Brands Hatch and finishing third in the Sebring 12-hours, Monza 1000 km and Spa 1000 km races. So far as Formula One was concerned, 1972 was a complete disaster. Driving a March for Frank Williams, Pescarolo was third in the non-championship Rothmans 50,000 at Brands Hatch, but in other races he was either poorly placed or retired. He crashed the

March at Monaco, Clermont Ferrand, Nürburgring, Österreichring and Monza and wrote-off Williams' new Politoys FX3-Ford at Brands Hatch. However, as compensation, he won the Le Mans 24-hours in a Matra 670 shared with Graham Hill and the Formula Two Mediterranean Grand Prix at Enna in Sicily in a Rondel Racing Brabham BT38-Ford.

Sports-car racing took priority in 1973, a year when Matra returned to this class full-time and clinched the World Championship of Makes. Pescarolo won the Vallelunga 6-hours, the Dijon 1000 km, the Le Mans 24-hours, the Österreichring 1000 km and the Watkins Glen 6-hours, each time partnered by Gérard Larrousse. In Formula Two, driving for the Motul-sponsored Rondel team, he won at Thruxton, while from his three Formula One appearances, the best he could muster was eighth with the ill-handling works March 721G/731-Ford in the Spanish Grand Prix.

With Motul sponsoring the works BRM team, it was back to Formula One full-time in 1974. However, it was yet another unsuccessful Grand Prix year for Pescarolo, the V12-engined British cars not proving competitive. His best placing was a fourth in the non-championship *Daily Express* Trophy at Silverstone and by the end of the year Pescarolo had quit the team. In sports-car racing there was another clean sweep for Pescarolo and Larrousse: the pair won the Imola 1000 km, the Le Mans 24-hours, the Österreichring 1000 km and the Kyalami six-hours. It marked Pescarolo's third successive victory at Le Mans, a feat only achieved twice before by Woolf Barnato (1928-9-30) and Olivier Gendebien (1960-1-2).

MK

SUPERSWEDE

THE GRAND PRIX racing driver of the 1950s was a completely different type of person from the man who raced the precision Formula One vehicle of the 60s and 70s, and many people agreed that there was less character in the sport than there had been a few years previously.

Drivers like Moss, Fangio, Collins and Hawthorn, protruding from their low-cut cockpits were instantly recognisable from the spectator enclosures, and were also well known for their exploits off the track. The shrewd businessman-cum-GP superstar of later years appeared to have no time for such frivolities, though, preferring to earn his six-figure fee and gracefully leave the scene. Despite this apparently too-professional approach, there still could be seen the individual driving style. There have been three basic styles of GP driver: the ones who have looked slow and trailed behind the rest; the ones who have looked steady but have been fast, like Fittipaldi, Clark and Stewart, and the ones that have looked *and gone* quickly. In the last-named group, the outstanding examples have been Jochen Rindt and a Swede named Bengt Ronald Peterson.

Ronnie, the son of an Orebo baker and engineer, was born on 14 February 1944 and, due to his father's exploits with 500 cc racers, soon got the taste for motor racing; in fact, he first went to see his father race when he was but four-years old. The remaining time in between then and his first kart race was spent with moto-cross and speedway-racing motor bikes. The first step into proper competition came when Ronnie's father built him a Yerman motor-cycle-engined kart with which Ronnie gained much success in three seasons of racing in the 200 cc class. After an even more successful time with a 100 cc kart, the graduation to Formula Three was made in 1966 with a home-built car called the SWVBB, a copy of the 1965 F3 Brabham.

Unfortunately, however, this enterprising venture was not very successful as the '66 Brabhams were that much more advanced. The only thing to do was to buy a proper Brabham, a BT18; this he did, and with the car he finished the season. In

his first race with the BT18, he was involved in a shunt which damaged the car's chassis. The car had to be used the following season and, although it was straightened out as much as possible, it still was not quite right; that year, Ronnie had to be content with thirds and fourths.

It was late 1967 when Peterson took the step that would ensure that his next mount would at least be up to the driver's not inconsiderable abilities. With friend, and soon-to-become racing sparring partner, Reine Wisell, he went off to Bologna to see the Pederzani brothers. The Pederzanis had been building karts since 1962 and were, by this time, building the cars to beat in F3, the Tecnos. Reine and Ronnie went home with expensive F3 cars in hand and, while Reine went around Europe racing, Ronnie concentrated on Swedish races for the '68 season, winning twelve out of 26 events and taking the Swedish Championship.

For 1969, a new Tecno with a Novamotor engine was purchased, and the car was raced under sponsorship from Vick, the coughdrop makers (who were, incidentally, to carry on sponsoring Ronnie for many seasons). There were numerous victories for Ronnie in 1969, and he went to the prestigious Formula Three event of the year, Monaco, with seven successive wins under his belt. A victory in the Principality always attracted plenty of notice in the right quarters, and Ronnie had a magnificent race against Reine's Chevron, coming out on top to win the event.

Late that same year, Peterson was contracted to drive a completely new car in F3; this was for March, who were taking their first tentative steps which were to lead to a quick jump to Formula One. The first race with the March 693 was at

Cadwell Park in England where Ronnie finished third. The next race at Montlhéry was not quite as successful: he ended up in a Paris hospital. The March directors went to see the dazed Peterson at his bedside and took him (along with customary flowers and grapes) a contract for Formula One in 1970.

Although Peterson was the first man to be signed for F1 with March, the experienced Amon and Siffert were to take the works drives. However, the Bicester company lined up a drive for Peterson in a private March 701, with Colin Crabbe's Antique Automobiles team.

The 701 chassis was relatively unproven and uncompetitive, with Stewart picking up the only Grand Prix win for March in Ken Tyrrell's team car in Spain. Peterson plodded through Formula One that year with seventh in Monaco as his highest placing. Driving the Malcolm Guthrie Racing Team March in Formula Two, he had a more encouraging time, although still far from brilliantly successful, finishing third in the European Trophy series by way of a number of good placings.

It was 1971 when the light from Sweden started to shine brightly. This was when March gave Ronnie a works drive in their STP-backed 711 as team leader. This car was a much lighter, more nimble and generally more competitive machine than its predecessor. The first race in which he showed the expected promise in F1 was at the Monaco GP, where he finished second to Stewart, only 25.6 seconds ahead. This was despite racing with suspected cracked ribs sustained from a nasty Silverstone shunt. After that, the season turned out well for Ronnie, overshadowed only by Stewart who was in great form. He came very close to winning his first

GP in Italy, but he had to be content with second place behind Peter Gethin's BRM which was all of one-hundredth of a second ahead. There was to be a fairly lean season in between that second place and his first GP win, although in Formula Two racing he quickly asserted himself as 'King' in the '71 season, taking the European Championship with the March 712.

1972 was the year of the ill-fated March 721X, the car that promised so much with its low polar moment of inertia. Despite the amazing handling this car promised (it probably would not have complemented Ronnie's style in the slightest, anyway), troubles with the gearbox linkage and other minor faults meant that it was virtually impossible to develop. So, the year was ended with Ronnie driving the 721G Formula Two chassis, specially converted. In fact, this car was quite successful: Ronnie started from the front row of the grid in Canada and led for a time, and in America he finished the race in fourth place.

However, the damage had been done and he had already made his mind up to leave. Colin Chapman was quickly on the scene and snapped up what was by now the hottest property on the motor-racing scene.

The position offered by John Player Team Lotus was 'joint number one' along with reigning World Champion Emerson Fittipaldi. This venture was quite successful considering the reputation Lotus had with many drivers. In his first seven GP starts in '73, he secured four pole positions, and in that seventh race, the Swedish GP at Anderstorp, Peterson beavered away through the field to lead his home GP, only to have a tyre deflate near the end and have to watch Denny Hulme's McLaren Ford pass him to win the race.

The next race saw Ronnie win his first GP, in France, and surely the first GP win must be the most elusive for any driver. This was so in Peterson's case for more victories came in Austria and Italy, where Fittipaldi was upset that Ronnie had not let him pass. That year in Formula Two, Ronnie and Emerson raced

Texaco Stars with Novamotor Jensen-Healey engines, but they were totally uncompetitive. Fittipaldi left the team at the end of the season and Jacky Ickx came in.

1974 was started with the ageing Lotus 72, but the new 76 with electric clutch and two brake-pedals was on the way. This car needed a great deal of development, however, and time could not always be found for this. 'One problem was that the 72 kept winning', said Ronnie, so obviously the team could not wholeheartedly keep testing the new machine. F1 wins at Monaco, one of Peterson's lucky circuits, France and Italy helped the season on, but by the end of

Bottom left: Ronnie Peterson made a comeback into Formula Two in 1975 at Thruxton. He is seen here facing the wrong way after spinning his Project 3 March 752. The ill-handling car was later badly damaged in a multiple shunt

Centre: Ronnie chats to Jody Scheckter in the Monaco pits in 1974; Peterson later beat Scheckter into second place in that race and also won the French GP. He is seen in France, *below right,* on his way to victory

the year it was Ronnie's driving that stopped the old 72 from being hopelessly outclassed.

It was then that talks were said to have started between former March and now Shadow team manager Alan Rees. During the 74–75 close season there was meant to be much negotiating between the two for Ronnie's services in one of the new quick cars of GP racing. When the storm clouds cleared, though, it seemed as if it was more of a bluff by Lotus to get its sponsors to give the team more money than a wish to move by the driver himself.

Early 1975 saw the 72 get probably its last breath when a new, lighter chassis was built. The car ran third in South Africa and finished third in the non-championship Race of Champions at Brands Hatch, and it was on the new Lotus model that was hoped would be ready later in the season that Peterson's hopes for the World Championship were pinned.

Throughout his career, Peterson has quickly adapted to every sort of car he has driven, flinging each more powerful model around just as he threw the karts around in Sweden to win six national titles. In other forms of racing he drove Ferrari sports cars with ex flat-mate and close friend Tim Schenken, drove for BMW in a few races during '74 and '75 and campaigned a Camaro in the International Race of Champions series. He expressed a dislike for Indy racing as it would not be much fun driving to strict orders from the pit around a boring oval circuit. While other GP superstars were busy relaxing around the world in the 1974–5 closed season, he was at home in Sweden pulling the crowds in for a local rallycross event driving a Volkswagen Beetle. In the event, he was lying in second place until clutch slip eliminated the car. It was not the money which attracted him to the rallycross, but the fun of it and the thought of getting more people to see the race. It is this enthusiasm and love for driving that has made Ronnie so competitive: you can only do something well if you enjoy doing it, and no one seems to have enjoyed race driving more than Ronnie Peterson. LJC

EVER SINCE the Edwardian heyday of Mme Camille Du Gast, lady drivers have added a touch of feminine glamour to motor sport. One of the most glamorous of all was Mrs Kay Petre, whose petite appearance concealed a steely determination to win, and which made her one of the outstanding racing drivers on the British scene in the 1930s.

Kay Petre started racing with sports cars, and during 1935 was one of an all-girl team at Brooklands, along with Aileen Ellison and Mrs Tolhurst. At the time, Sammy Davis commented: 'A distinctly decorative appearance and turnout disguised a toughness, and tenacity, that was as unexpected as it was magnificent. If she had orders to hold a certain speed, or drive so many hours, all creation could not have stopped her doing it, whether a large car at 130 mph or a small one at 90 mph was involved. This had been most noticable in two Monte Carlo Rallies where she had been one of the crew, for on each occasion she lasted through the three days and four nights of driving without turning a hair.'

Quite apart from her track performance, you could not help noticing Kay Petre: in July 1936, she arrived for her first Donington meeting in the 'luxurious magnificence' of a huge Morris in concours condition painted in the same livery as her supercharged Riley. The press recorded: 'Mrs Petre made a fine start, but was outmatched for the nonce.' The following week, the elegant Kay was on her way to take part in the Ramsgate Concours d'Elegance.

She had already earned a place in Brooklands history, lapping in the big 10½-litre V12 Delage at almost 135 mph, the second-fastest speed at Brooklands achieved by a lady driver (the fastest was Gwenda Hawkes, whose time in the Derby-Maserati equalled virtually 136 mph).

The 1937 season saw Mrs Petre as one of the official Austin works team, driving a side-valve Austin racer, while Dodson and Hadley handled the new ohc cars. The team's first official outing was the 1937 British Empire Trophy meeting at Brooklands, but all three were forced to retire, Kay Petre's car developing accelerator trouble.

However, the cars appeared again a few weeks later at Shelsley Walsh, where the Austin team carried off all the honours in the 750 cc class, making the first, second, third, fourth and fifth fastest times. Kay Petre's time of 46.9 seconds, fourth fastest in the class, was especially noteworthy compared with Bert Hadley's new class record, as Hadley was piloting the new ohc model, and Kay Petre's car was the side-valve.

Later the same month (June), the Austin team lineup was Hadley (ohc), Goodacre (ohc) and Kay Petre (sv). The supercharged Austins were scratch cars, giving 40½ minutes to limit man H. B. Shaw (Salmson), who completed 25 laps before Hadley was allowed to start.

Hadley's stint included a new 750 cc class record lap of 121.68 mph, and by the time Goodacre took over, the team had come from the back of the field to fifth place. Goodacre turned in consistent lap speeds of 118 mph, so that when Kay Petre set off, after 70 laps, the team was lying second. On the 80th lap, though, the oil gauge on her car's dashboard suddenly began to leak scalding hot oil into the cockpit of the Austin as she was in the lead.

Regardless of the discomfort, Kay Petre held

Above: Kay Petre at Brooklands in 1935; she was later to become one of the most famous woman drivers of all time and to establish herself as a serious and competitive performer

A touch of class

on to the lead with lap speeds of 100 mph-plus, expecting all the while that the engine would seize from lack of oil pressure. However, her luck held, and the Austin team won the relay with an overall average of 105.63 mph, 15 mph faster than the record held by Morgan since 1934, and well ahead of the second team, MG, who averaged 85.8 mph.

On 13 June 1937, Kay Petre was one of the works team which gave the Austin Nippies their Le Mans début, but the unblown Jamieson-modified cars suffered from teething troubles, and failed to figure in the results (although, rebodied, they subsequently enjoyed considerable acclaim in trials and rallies under the new name of Grasshopper).

It was as the Grasshopper that these cars were entered for the 12-hour race at Donington that year, taking second, third and fifth places, the latter position falling to Kay Petre and her co-driver P. Stevenson.

In the Crystal Palace Cup on 15 August, plug

trouble spoiled Kay Petre's chance of coming second in the 15-lap Crystal Palace Cup, but at Shelsley Walsh a month later, she climbed the course in 43.78 seconds to earn the Ladies Challenge Trophy.

While practicing for the Brooklands BRDC 500 miles event that month, Kay Petre was travelling at 90 mph when her car was struck by Reg Parnell's MG, which had been travelling too high up the banking. The little Austin rolled, and Mrs Petre was taken to hospital with severe concussion.

Thereafter, she devoted herself to writing about motoring for the *Daily Sketch*, but here, too, tragedy struck, for in the 1939 Monte Carlo Rally, she and Major Reggie Empson were following the competitors through France when their car was hit by a lorry at a crossroad; Empson was killed and Mrs Petre was injured. However, she continued her career after the war, becoming one of the first members of the Guild of Motoring Writers. DBW

AT FIRST GLANCE it would seem astonishingly rapid progress that allowed motoring pioneer Gottlieb Daimler to have a petrol engine running in the early 1880s, considering that the first oil well was sunk in Pennsylvania as late as 1859. We must remember, however, that man was distilling oils from coal before that: he had to, for the supply of whale oil was drying up as the unfortunate creatures were hunted down. Alas, to most of the races of man it came more naturally to be hunters than to be scientists; yet there were some who had been exploiting for thousands of years the world's natural mineral oils. Rock oils, they became called—and eventually the Latinists translated that

Black Gold

Deep within the earth lies the crude oil from which is extracted much of the world's energy and a number of valuable by-products. Without this precious crude oil, most of the world's cars and much of its industry would grind to a halt

into *petroleum*, the word we use today for a substance that seems to lie not only beneath the ground, but also at the very roots of most modern technologies. In fact it was not the mechanised parts of the world, but the civilised, that knew it first: the Chinese drilled for oil, using percussion bits tipping bamboo pipes, more than two thousand years ago; and long before that it had been used where it seeped out of the ground (around the Black Sea and the Caspian) for heating, cooking, cementing bricks and caulking boats.

That area is still one of the richest in petroleum; but the stuff occurs all over the world, wherever the ground is sedimentary rather than igneous or volcanic. So long as it occurs underground and is an organic (containing carbon) fluid, it is petroleum—regardless of whether it be thick or thin, sweet-smelling or foully sulphurous, black or red or yellow; some kinds even fluoresce green or purple in reflected light. Each deposit of crude oil is a highly individual mixture: its unique characteristics probably could not be exactly matched by any other crude oil in the world, even one found a few hundred yards further along or just a few feet further down.

The variety of crude oils is truly amazing. Road-maker's asphalt comes from a huge lake of tar in

Above: the multi-coloured insignia of some major motor-spirit distributors

Left: Edwin L. Drake, right, who sunk the first successful oil well at Titusville, Pennsylvania, in 1859; he is seen talking to Peter Wilson, a local druggist, with 'Uncle' Billie Smith, his head driller, on the extreme right of the background

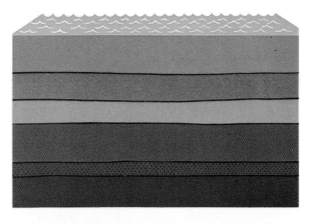

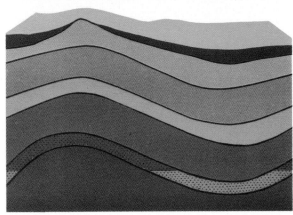

Right: in the top illustration the beginnings of oil formation are shown; layers of mud form on the seabed, burying the remains of myriad sea creatures and eventually turning into rock. In the lower illustration, oil has formed, by a process not fully understood, under the non-porous rock (in the red parts); volcanic action has caused the layers to distort, thus trapping the oil

Right: a schematic diagram showing the component parts of an oil pumping well

Below: a few of the products which are derived, either directly or indirectly from oil. From left to right and top to bottom they are insecticides, dry cleaning materials, detergents, synthetic fibres, fertilisers, plastics, synthetic rubber, wax products, paints, cosmetics and roofing and flooring materials

The complexities of these assorted petroleum compounds are still not wholly unravelled, despite the wealth and expertise of the industry; but basically they are all hydrocarbons, in which the major constituents are carbon (85–90%) and hydrogen, with minor quantities of three other elements—sulphur, nitrogen, and oxygen—and minute traces of substances such as vanadium, nickel, chlorine, arsenic and so forth, albeit in perhaps only a few parts per billion.

It is from these crude oils that, by refining processes becoming yearly more complex, the petroleum industry produces complex mixtures that we use for generating power (gasolines and diesel oils, for examples) or heat, for making lubricants or roads, or for the bases of countless chemicals used in plastics, synthetic rubbers, and thousands of other end products ranging the scale of civilised uses from medicines to explosives, fertilizers to herbicides, aphrodisiacs to

Trinidad, and there is a similar vast deposit of bitumen at Athabasca in Canada; both are very heavy oils, so viscous as to be semi-solid, and it is only because they do not flow freely that the modern oil industry does not normally include them among petroleum crudes. By the same criterion they exclude shale oil, which does not flow from its rock matrix at all unless the stone be strongly heated. At the other end of the scale are deposits so light and free from non-distillable residues that they are excluded too; and at this point the petroleum may be so volatile (boiling points vary from 20 or 30 to several hundred degrees Celsius) that it is gaseous, although light liquid mixtures can be re-recovered from gas fields.

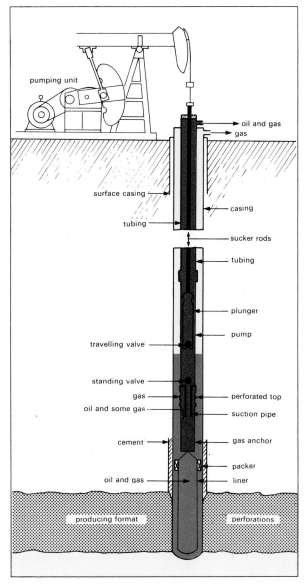

feather-pluckers. Almost all petroleum products have to be tailored to meet exacting market requirements and a lot of blending of crudes is done to provide the distillers and refiners with a base having the necessary properties.

The blend can be broken down by distillation into a series of 'cuts' or fractions. The heavier fractions can then be broken down further, by 'cracking' techniques in which complex and heavy molecules are broken up

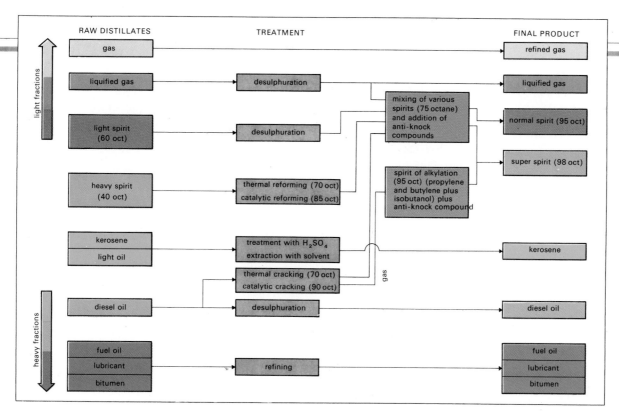

Left: a schematic diagram, showing how various fractions of oil are further refined and mixed

into simpler and lighter ones, to produce lighter and generally more valuable commodities such as motor spirit. The fuel that the motorist buys from the service station pump is more than simple petroleum distillate, much more: the number and variety of additives is large and variable, some of them being themselves end-products of the petrochemical industry (such as the lead compounds that give our 'petrol' better anti-knock properties) and some deriving from the gases given off during distillation (such as butane, which is added to gasoline to improve its volatility). It is not even necessary that the motorist's standby be based on petroleum: some of the highest-octane varieties are not, while more ordinary ones can be made from coal. Petrol is what the English motorist calls it, however—and the word is a sound enough clue to the origins of most of it. Men in the industry detest the word, of course, and will adopt any jargon that frees them from the popular tyranny of what began as a proprietary name: gasoline and motor spirit are preferred, however quaint they seem.

However named, the stuff is an important product of the petroleum industry, although not the biggest. In Britain, it accounted for only 15% of all petroleum crude imported in 1974; in other countries the proportion may differ somewhat, according to the relative popularities of diesel and petrol engines, the availability of other fuels such as coal or other energy sources such as upland water, and so on.

There are many criteria by which a motor gasoline may be approved or rejected. The volatility that we have already mentioned may have to be adjusted cyclically each year: it is a question of balancing the ingredients to create a blend that is volatile enough to allow easy starting and rapid warm-up, yet not so quick to evaporate as to cause vapour-lock difficulties on a warm day. The smell must be acceptable: this can be dealt with by additional treatment processes, as can any tendency to form gummy deposits in the manifold system.

Much the most important characteristics of a motor spirit—from the viewpoints of the driver and of the refinery—is its anti-knock value or 'octane number'. This is determined with the aid of a standardised laboratory test engine, in which the test sample is matched with a blend of two pure reference

fuels: one is heptane, which is terribly knock-prone and is rated at 0 on the arbitrary 'octane number' scale, and the other is iso-octane which is rated at 100. If the intensity of knock produced by the test sample is the same as that given by a mixture of 93% iso-octane and 7% heptane, it would be described as a 93 octane number fuel. Today, synthetic fuels and additives may rate octane numbers higher than 100, which suggests a nonsensical 100-plus percentage of iso-octane and a negative percentage of heptane—a situation never envisaged when the scale was established. In this case the reference standard is made by adding tetraethyl lead to iso-octane.

There are two standard test procedures, differing not only in engine speed but also in mixture temperature. The less relevant to modern car operation is the Research method, but the figure it yields (identified as RON, for Research Octane Number) is preferred commercially—because it is higher—to the MON rating measured by the Motor method. Attention today is focussed on minimising the difference between the two, the 'sensitivity number' which may be as low as 5 whereas a decade ago it might well have been 10—as in the case of a fuel of 96 RON and 86 MON ratings.

Nothing like these figures could be achieved by a fuel simply distilled from a crude oil as what is called a 'straight-run' fraction. Any attempt to do so, by distillation at the appropriate boiling point for a motor spirit (which for practical reasons is generally between 30° and 200°C) might yield a fuel whose RON rating was as low as 50, as was the case in the pioneer days of motoring when gasolines varied greatly according to the provenance of the crude oils from which they were cut. In a modern car such stuff would cause unbearable knock, so the refinery processes have to include the manufacture of concentrates of the high-octane hydrocarbons—which include aromatics, olefins and isoparaffins.

The earliest method for improving the octane number of a gasoline was to create olefins, by a process that was called thermal cracking: the oil was simply heated until it started to decompose, the large molecules being 'cracked' or broken into smaller ones by the heat. This worked quite well on distillates at the high end of the gasoline range of boiling points, especially in the range 15°–250°C which are known as kerosenes.

For the naphthas, which boil at lower temperatures in the desired gasoline range, the heating was done under high pressure (as much as 1000 lb per sq in or 70 kg per sq cm) in which conditions the hydrocarbons break down into smaller groups which then recombine as higher-octane versions. These are the aromatics, and the process is called thermal reforming. Nowadays more effective methods replace these: catalysts (including platinum and fuller's earth or synthetic substitutes) are used in reforming and cracking; and the isoparaffins depend on modern processes such as alkylation, which gave us the very high octane aviation gasolines.

A further way to attain high anti-knock values is to throw in appropriate additives. The American scientist Thomas Midgley started this in about 1927, and effective lead compounds (tetraethyl) and tetramethyl leads, TEL and TML respectively) were soon found capable of increasing octane numbers by 5–10 when added to motor spirit in quite small proportions, perhaps 0.06% or less by volume. The American lawyer Ralph Nader may prove to have finished it, although he cannot take all the credit for the modern interest in pollution problems that has led to a review of the effects of lead in exhaust emissions and of the cost of doing without these additives.

Current marketing demands the manufacture of motor spirits at not less than two RON levels, representing premium and regular grades. Increasing attention is also being given to what is loosely called 'road octane number', a rating thought by the producers to be more relevant to the realities of modern high-speed multi-cylinder engines than the old RON and MON numbers derived from slower single-cylinder test engines. The problem is complicated by variations and discrepancies between one engine and another; but the basic approach is to aim for a uniform distribution of high-octane components throughout the whole boiling range of a gasoline.

This is because of the behaviour of the fuel in the inlet manifold when an engine is being accelerated, which involves the delivery of the carburettor's richest mixture. What happens is that liquid fuel is deposited on the internal surfaces of the manifold, often as a continuous film, from which particles evaporate and are drawn by the airstream into the cylinders. Unfortunately, it is the more volatile fractions that are most likely to be taken straight into the cylinders, while the 'heavier' (higher boiling point) fractions lag behind, staying in liquid form on the

Below: a drawing showing the various parts of a modern oil refinery situated on the coast or on a major river

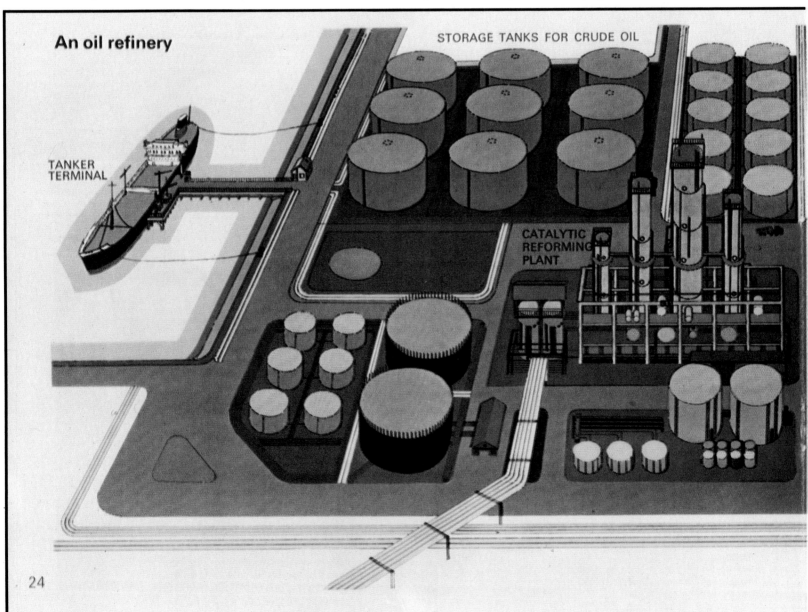

An oil refinery

STORAGE TANKS FOR CRUDE OIL

TANKER TERMINAL

CATALYTIC REFORMING PLANT

24

manifold wall. It is therefore important that the volatile fractions should be of sufficiently high octane number to prevent knocking occurring in these conditions.

Not all automotive fuels are plagued by octane number requirements. The laboratory test of a diesel fuel will evoke instead a cetane number, on the face of it measuring knock in the same way but arriving by a very different route. The refiners' main problems in making fuel for high-speed diesel engines (the big marine and stationary diesels that run at very low speeds are much more easily satisfied, and happily accept rough stuff containing asphaltic residues) are associated with ignition quality, low-temperature behaviour and sulphur content.

The fuel required for an automotive diesel is based on petroleum distillates in the 200–350°C boiling range, and thus overlaps a little with kerosene. It was originally used to make 'carburetted water gas' with which to enrich supplies of town gas made from coke, and so it is widely known as gas oil, although in Britain the abbreviation DERV (for Diesel Engine Road Vehicle) is popular. In its diesel application, the important factor is the time taken for the fuel to begin to burn after it has been injected into the combustion

chamber. A good diesel fuel should begin to burn in several places within this space within a very short time after injection. If the delay were too great, the whole charge might fire simultaneously, causing violent combustion tantamount to explosive detonation, with correspondingly heavy knock.

In the test engine, the ignition delay is measured in degrees of crankshaft rotation, and the performance of the fuel sample is compared with reference to blends of a paraffin called cetane and an aromatic compound named alpha-methyl naphthalene. The cetane number is thus obtained by similar means to the gasoline octane number—and its importance yields a clue to the cause of sundry political problems. Cetane is a simple paraffin, and paraffins display better ignition quality than aromatic fuels. It so happens that crude petroleum from the Middle East is highly paraffinic, and is therefore eagerly sought as the source of good diesel fuels, especially in Europe where the diesel engine is so much more prevalent than elsewhere.

It is the wax content that determines the low-temperature characteristics of a diesel fuel. When it gets cold, the wax separates in crystals that can choke the fuel line and starve the engine. As for sulphur content (the third of the diesel criteria mentioned

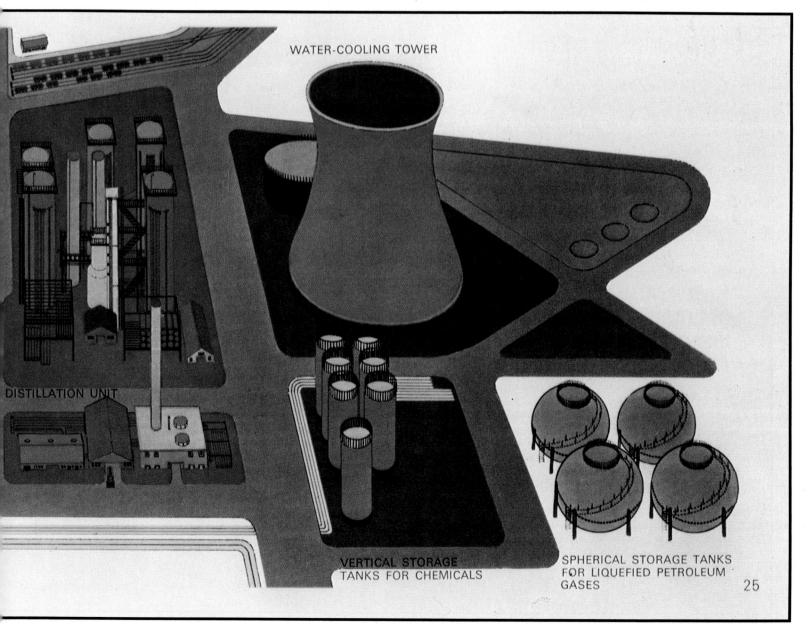

WATER-COOLING TOWER

DISTILLATION UNIT

VERTICAL STORAGE TANKS FOR CHEMICALS

SPHERICAL STORAGE TANKS FOR LIQUEFIED PETROLEUM GASES

25

earlier) it is thought to aggravate engine wear and the formation of deposits, though how much difference it makes is still a matter for argument. Whatever the truth of the matter, the market now demands low sulphur levels, so refineries dealing with crudes containing high percentages (the figure occasionally reaches 7, although 0.2–3% is the usual range) have to remove the excess sulphur by additional processes.

After the petroleum has given up its motor spirit, its kerosene, and its gas oil, what is left may be distilled under vacuum to produce a series of waxy 'cuts' that form the basis of lubricating oils. These are purified in stages by solvents that get rid in turn of waxes, aromatics, and unstable materials that might cause corrosion and provoke sludge formation. After that, the evolution of a high-grade motor oil involves the search for mutually compatible base stocks and additives to control viscosity, volatility, corrosion, sludging, film strength, and many other properties.

The sensitivity of a lubricating oil to the interaction and interdependence of its ingredients and their working environment is typical, on a restricted scale, of the political and environmental sensitivity of the entire petroleum industry. A useful illustration is the effect of emission controls on roadholding! Under pressure from environmentalists on the one hand, to eliminate the lead compounds on which they relied for good anti-knock properties, and from the motor

Above right: an artist's impression of production platform Brent 'A', showing its size compared with that of St Paul's Cathedral in London; this platform was built for use in the North Sea 125 miles north-east of Lerwick in the Shetland Isles

Above left: one of the modern North Sea oil rigs, belonging to the Shell company

industry and energy-source conservers on the other hand, to maintain supplies of high-octane motor spirit, the petroleum industry has had to divert to gasoline production large quantities of styrene, which can be used (at no little cost) to restore some of the properties that vanish with the lead. The consequent shortage of styrene has made it very difficult to the rubber industry to maintain supplies of a synthetic polymer known as styrene butadiene rubber (SBR) which is more responsible than anything else for the outstanding wet grip and abrasion resistance of modern tyres. In fact the only common tread compounds to offer even more grip are variants based on an extra-high styrene content (originally devised for soling footwear in 1946) or on 'extension' of the SBR with a larger than normal proportion of oil—and since the oil used in rubber production is also derived from petroleum, the latter of these alternatives is hardly better in times of acute availability problems.

Whether there is or (as seems at the time of writing to be more likely) is not a shortage of oil, the rate at which we use it is quite astonishing. The industry has grown phenomenally fast: when Pennsylvania's first well was sunk by Colonel Drake, output was equivalent to 6000 barrels a year. That was in 1859; in 1860 the output was already 500,000 barrels. Now the world output runs into billions of barrels, at 35 gallons a time! LJKS

Motor racing's most successful family?

THE HISTORY OF NASCAR racing is both action packed and colourful, and it is a great shame that it has never been seen on European tracks. It is a sport peculiar to America, though, using as it does large-engined saloon cars with, what would appear at first sight to be, fairly standard bodies, albeit with no side windows. There is a great deal more to it than that: Nascar constructors are probably the most successful rule-benders in the world, and in any case the sport has evolved to a situation where the cars are really as close to standard production cars as they are to steam-rollers. Although it might share the same basic engine, the NASCAR stocker will be capable of reaching speeds of up to 190 mph, and that engine will have been developed to produce close to 600 horsepower.

Naturally it was not always thus and, in the early days, they were a lot closer to living up to their names—stock cars.

The National Association for Stock Car Auto Racing, to give it its full title, officially came into being in February 1948. Its founder and leading light until a few years ago was one Bill France, who later handed over full control of the NASCAR operation to his son, William Junior.

It was at one of NASCAR's early races, at Charlotte Raceway on 19 June 1949, that the name of Lee Petty first went onto a results sheet. He came second that day, and went on to win the NASCAR Grand National Championship three times. By 1975, only one man had beaten that record, and his name was Petty, too.

As the influence of NASCAR spread, so those first stock-car drivers—many of whom were reported to have gained their skill while trying to outrun 'Revenooers' in pursuit of their illicit whisky trade—had to travel further and further afield in the search for prize money. Lee Petty, along with other famous drivers like Fireball Roberts, Curtis Turner, Joe Weatherly and so on, would drive overnight from one meeting to the next, trailing their race cars behind their trucks and having only their wives for company. The sport was strongest by far in the Southern states, and this is where the majority of top drivers have come from over the years. The track that has come to be regarded as the home of NASCAR is at Daytona Beach in Florida—first on the beach itself and, from 1959, on a new banked track conveniently located just a little further from the sea. It was Lee Petty who won the very first Daytona 500 race on this new track—it was also here that he had his biggest and most spectacular accident, which led to his retirement.

Lee was not a particularly flamboyant driver, not when compared with the likes of Curtis

Above: probably the most successful father and son team in motor sport, Lee Petty (*left*) and his son Richard (*right*) have dominated NASCAR racing for many years

Turner and Fireball Roberts, anyway. He usually won races with skilful and steady driving, although if other drivers ever mistook this for timidity, they usually discovered their mistake the hard way. His accidents, though, were spectacular. History records that during one race on the old beach circuit at Daytona, his windscreen became so caked with sand that he lost sight of the track completely and drove straight out to sea! Realising his error, he rejoined the race to the astonishment of several other drivers on that part of the track, who were not mentally prepared for the sight of his big blue Dodge returning from the waves at full blast. There was rather a fine accident as a result, involving Ralph Moody, who recovered to come third!

Lee's car was always blue, and carried the number 42 which was allocated to him for his entire career. Up until 1957, he always drove a Dodge, but in that year he made the switch to Oldsmobile. 1957 was also the year of what was possibly his most controversial victory. While tussling for the lead with Curtis Turner, it seems he somehow helped Turner's car into the wall. He did not win, as it happens, but the incident

caused a certain amount of acrimony in the Ford camp, as Turner had been driving the only surviving Ford in the race!

1958 was a good year for Lee, though. He won the Grand National Championship for the second time, his race record including nine outright wins for Oldsmobile. He also won the NASCAR short-track championship. In 1958, too, he competed against his son Richard for the very first time. Junior blew his engine, but Pa won the race.

1959 saw Lee take that Grand National title for the third and final time. He had fourteen victories that year, four with his Oldsmobile and ten with a new Plymouth. 1960, though, started badly, when he got beaten by his son, who took third place at Daytona to Lee's fourth! All in all, it was not a particularly successful year for Lee. 1961, though, was worse. In a qualifying race for the Daytona 500, he tangled with another competitor on one of the high-speed banked turns, and they both went clean over the banking to crash forty feet onto the ground below. Those NASCAR cars were pretty tough even in those days, and Lee got away with injuries restricted to his legs, while the other driver was virtually unhurt. Lee's career was virtually ended by this incident—he did race a few more times but professed that he did not care for it anymore.

So, it was left to Richard to keep the Petty name at the forefront. He had obviously had a good grounding, having attended meetings with his father for many years before getting to race himself. Unlike most fathers, Lee had actively encouraged his son to race, and kept that encouragement up even when his son started off his career with a series of impressive crashes. Richard's first recognition came in 1958, when he was dubbed NASCAR 'Rookie of the Year'.

1963 was his first year of real success, though. He did not win the Grand National Championship—Joe Weatherly just snatched it from him at the last race of the season. However, out of nineteen Plymouth victories that year, he won fourteen, and his revenge was to come the following year, when he became Champion for the first time and earned almost $100,000 in prize money. 1965 and '66 were not so good, although he did win Daytona again the latter year. 1967, however, was probably his best year

ever. He won the Championship together with over $130,000 in prize money, and took ten straight victories in a row. He raced forty-eight times, finished forty-one, and won twenty-seven. In 1971 and '72, he won the Championship again, much to the delight of the STP Corporation who were his new sponsors after the Chrysler factory had withdrawn their support in 1970. Apparently, the Petty team was a little reluctant to change the colour of their car from blue to STP red, but at least they were allowed to continue to use the famous 43 racing number allocated to Richard.

In 1975, the Petty team was based at Randleman in North Carolina, and it was here that the Petty workshops were also based. It was a family business with Lee still involved, and so were Richard's brother Maurice and cousin Dale. Richard himself placed a great deal of importance in the family aspect of the team, and said that it was that which made it all worthwhile for him. He preferred to direct accolades for success to the team in general rather than accept them for himself alone, and was surprisingly modest about his achievements, saying that none of it would have been possible if it was not for the ex-

tremely high standard of preparation the car got.

It was also interesting to note that Richard just did not want to know about any other forms of motor racing apart from those big American stock cars. He was offered single-seater Grand Prix drives and Indianapolis cars to race, but he always turned them down with little hesitation. Stock cars were what he knew and lived for, and it seemed he would be reluctant to try anything that might tempt him away from the cars and the life and the friendship that he saw as being an integral part of the NASCAR scene.

In 1975, Richard was 38 years old, but he did not race until he was 21—that was his father's only stipulation about his involvement with the sport. In those seventeen years, he won almost two million dollars all told—probably as much as any other racing driver in the world. He also won around 170 races—a fantastic record by anyone's standards.

Richard and Lee Petty are the only father and son team to have done so well in any form of motor sport, writing their names in the racing history books so many times that they are unlikely ever to be surpassed.   AA

Below: Richard Petty and his STP Dodge in action at Daytona in 1975. The Petty family has been a major force in NASCAR racing for many years

This magnificent four-color encyclopedia is brought to you by Columbia House in cooperation with Orbis Publishing Ltd., one of Great Britain's most enterprising publishers. Rather than change any of the encylopedia's authoritative international automotive text, we have included a glossary of terms that will give you immediate American equivalents, a conversion table for the international metric system, and a conversion table for equivalent monetary values.

Glossary

BRITISH	AMERICAN	BRITISH	AMERICAN
Aerial	Antenna	Motor	Engine
Aluminium	Aluminum	Number plate	License plate
Apron	Skirt	Overrider	Bumper guard
Big-end	Rod (conrod) bearing	Paraffin	Kerosene
Blower (colloquial)	Supercharger	Parking brake	Parking lock
Bonnet	Hood	Petrol	Gasoline, "gas"
Boot	Trunk	Petrol pump	Gasoline or fuel pump
Brake servo	Power brake	Production car	Stock car
Bulkhead	Firewall	Propellor shaft	Drive shaft
Capacity	Displacement	Quarter light	Door vent
Carburetter; carburettor	Carburetor		
Check strap	Door stop	Rear lamp	Tail light
Clutch release bearing	Clutch throwout bearing	Rear seat squab	Rear setback or backrest
Control box	Voltage regulator	Reverse lamp	Back up light
Crown wheel and pinion	Ring gear and pinion	Roof lamp	Dome light
Cylinder block	Cylinder crankcase	Saloon	Sedan
Dip switch	Dimmer switch	Scuttle	Cowl
Door pillar	Door post	Selector rod	Shift bar
Drop arm	Pitman arm	Servo-assisted	Power assisted
Drop-head	Convertible	Side lamp	Parking light
Dynamo	Generator	Side member	Side rail
Epicylic gearbox	Planetary gearbox	Spanner	Wrench
Exhaust silencer	Muffler	Sparking plug	Spark plug
		Starting handle	Crank handle
Facia panel	Dashboard	Steering column	Steering post
Gear lever	Gear shift lever	Steering relay	Steering idler
Gearbox	Transmission	Stub axle	Steering knuckle
Gearbox housing	Transmission casing	Sump	Pan
Gearchange	Gearshift	Swivel pin	King pin
Glassfibre	Fiberglass	Toe board	Toe pan
Grease nipple	Grease fitting	Track	Tread
Gudgeon pin	Piston or wrist pin	Track rod	Tie bar or track bar
Half shaft	Axle shaft	Two-stroke	Two-cycle
Handbrake	Parking brake	Tyre	Tire
Hose clip	Hose clamp	Valance	Rocker panel
Ignition harness	Ignition set	Wheel arch	Wheelhouse or housing
Kerb	Curb	Wheel brace	Wheel wrench
Layshaft	Counter shaft	Windscreen	Windshield
		Wing	Fender
Main shaft	Output shaft	Wishbone	A-arm; Control arm
Marque	Brand, make	Works	Plant, factory

Metric Equivalents
(Based on National Bureau of Standards)

Length

Centimeter (Cm.)	= 0.3937 in.	In.	= 2.5400 cm.
Meter (M.)	= 3.2808 ft.	Ft.	= 0.3048 m.
Meter	= 1.0936 yd.	Yd.	= 0.9144 m.
Kilometer (Km.)	= 0.6214 mile	Mile	= 1.6093 km.

Area

Sq. cm.	= 0.1550 sq. in.	Sq. in.	= 6.4516 sq. cm.
Sq. m.	= 10.7639 sq. ft.	Sq. ft.	= 0.0929 sq. m.
Sq. m.	= 1.1960 sq. yd.	Sq. yd.	= 0.8361 sq. m.
Hectare	= 2.4710 acres	Acre	= 0.4047 hectar
Sq. km.	= 0.3861 sq. mile	Sq. mile	= 2.5900 sq. km.

Volume

Cu. cm.	= 0.0610 cu. in.	Cu. in.	= 16.3872 cu. cm.
Cu. m.	= 35.3145 cu. ft.	Cu. ft.	= 0.0283 cu. m.
Cu. m.	= 1.3079 cu. yd.	Cu. yd.	= 0.7646 cu. m.

Capacity

Liter	= 61.0250 cu. in.	Cu. in.	= 0.0164 liter
Liter	= 0.0353 cu. ft.	Cu. ft.	= 28.3162 liters
Liter	= 0.2642 gal. (U.S.)	Gal.	= 3.7853 liters
Liter	= 0.0284 bu. (U.S.)	Bu.	= 35.2383 liters

$$\text{Liter} = \begin{cases} 1000.027 \text{ cu. cm.} \\ 1.0567 \text{ qt. (liquid) or } 0.9081 \text{ qt. (dry)} \\ 2.2046 \text{ lb. of pure water at } 4\ C = 1 \text{ kg.} \end{cases}$$

Weight

Gram. (Gm.)	= 15.4324 grains	Grain	= 0.0648 gm.
Gram	= 0.0353 oz.	Oz.	= 28.3495 gm.
Kilogram (Kg.)	= 2.2046 lb.	Lb.	= 0.4536 kg.
Kg.	= 0.0011 ton (sht.)	Ton (sht.)	= 907.1848 kg.
Ton (met.)	= 1.1023 ton (sht.)	Ton (sht.)	= 0.9072 ton (met.)
Ton (met.)	= 0.9842 ton (lg.)	Ton (lg.)	= 1.0160 ton (met.)

Pressure

1 kg. per sq. cm.	= 14.223 lb. per sq. in.
1 lb. per sq. in.	= 0.0703 kg. per sq. cm.
1 kg. per sq. m.	= 0.2048 lb. per sq. ft.
1 lb. per sq. ft.	= 4.8824 kg. per sq. m.
1 kg. per sq. cm.	= 0.9678 normal atmosphere

$$1 \text{ normal atmosphere} = \begin{cases} 1.0332 \text{ kg. per sq. cm.} \\ 1.0133 \text{ bars} \\ 14.696 \text{ lb. per sq. in.} \end{cases}$$

Approximate Values of the Pound (£)
in terms of U.S. Dollars ($)

1914-1919	$4.76
1935	4.90
1936	4.97
1937	4.94
1938	4.89
1939	4.46
1940-1949	4.03
1950-1967	2.80
1968-1970	2.40
1971-1972	$2.40/2.60
1972-Present	2.60/2.10